IN THE END, IT WAS ALL ABOUT LOVE.

MUSA OKWONGA

First published in 2021
by Rough Trade Books

First Edition

ISBN 978-1-912722-93-8

Design by Craig Oldham
Cover Art by Daniel Mather
Printed in England

roughtradebooks.com

THIS IS A JOURNEY IN THREE PARTS.

In the first part, you visit Berlin;
in the second part, you visit Dr. Oppong;
and in the third part, you visit the homeland.

PART ONE:
Righteous Migrants

PART TWO:
Black Gravity

PART THREE:
Your Passport

PART ONE:
Righteous Migrants

What happened to the winds that sent the slave ships?
Some of these gusts are proud that they filled those ancient sails.
You could hear them above Berlin on election night,
Hailing the arrival of the moonlight and far-right;
You could hear them whistling through the corridors
Of the Holocaust memorial, slapping its stone walls and floors,
Gasping applause.

What happened to the winds that sent the slave ships?
Some of these breezes, still thick with guilt,
Now speed refugees towards Europe;
Impatient to atone,
They toss yet more dark bodies into the foam.

What happened to the winds that sent the slave ships?
Some of this air is in the best of health,
Since it has forgiven itself:
I was simply swept along by the prevailing mood,
There was nothing I could do.

What happened to the winds that sent the slave ships?
Some of these hurricanes remain enraged;
You can hear them in the chests of activists
Who stand across from fascists in Spandau:
They are the howls of every African child, woman and man drowned.
These winds have always resisted
With every major and minor breath—
Whether forming storms that left the slaver's ship a wreck
Or sending mischievous wafts to blow the hats from masters' heads.

What happened to the winds that sent the slave ships?
None of them have retired:
They've migrated to Germany in their millions,
And you can find the righteous ones
Whispering through its capital city at weekends,
Slipping through a window to cool a queer couple after a long afternoon
of love:
Or sighing through the barbecues at Tempelhofer Feld,
Content that there is still a world that knows how freedom smells.

Berlin Is Not Germany.

Sooner or later Berlin will punch you in the stomach. When it does, please try not to take this personally—instead, try to treat it as a passport stamp, as a sign of your arrival. You won't get on here if you don't. If you hang around long enough, it will give you a kiss on the forehead, it will invite you to the less harsh parts of itself.

You won't know when the blow is coming or where the blow is coming from, but if it takes over a year to strike then you should be highly suspicious. The longer you wait, the more likely it is to be cataclysmic: there is a good chance that, like an inefficient yet vengeful tax collector, it is merely getting ready to collect an epic debt.

Berlin is not Germany, people will tell you. What they mean, of course, is that Berlin is not like the rest of Germany. But Berlin is deeply German. If each of this country's towns are members of the same family, then Berlin is merely the mischievous sibling that ran away from home. While Munich and Frankfurt each got themselves a mortgage, Berlin hooked up with an older partner and took a couple of bar jobs.

Berlin is not a city for grown-ups. They will say that, and think it is true, but they are wrong. Berlin is often terrifyingly adult. Innocence doesn't linger here. To survive here, you need to be at least half wolf. What they mean is: Berlin is as volatile as an angry adolescent. Other cities can't match its emotional extremes. To live in Berlin, you must actually have something of the parent about you—you need to tolerate the town as it surges through its range of mood swings.

Ah, mood swings. Though Berlin is a place of extreme seasons, this city's divergent turns are not confined to the weather. Its inhabitants will shock you with acts of rudeness and kindness, often in the course of the same day. For that reason, you might find Berlin addictive. If so, that's because it's both too much and not nearly enough. You can saturate yourself in this city, but still find yourself deprived.

People will often ask what brought you to Berlin—and they will often ask it in just those words, as if you were summoned here. Perhaps, in some sense, you were. Living in Berlin, if not quite a calling, is compelling. It takes a particular breed to come here, and a different sort altogether to stay. Soon enough, this city will tell you which type you are.

***

What Brought You To Berlin?

Everyone asks you this. You answer glibly—that you came here to do four things: to write during the day, to see your friends during the evening, to fall in love, and to stay in love.

But that's not the root of it. You came here to disappear. For the first few months you are in Berlin you are largely invisible, or at least as invisible as a dark-skinned black man in an overwhelmingly white city can be. The colours of your clothes mimic those of the city: concrete, tarmac, plaster. You wish to be as innocuous as a cobblestone.

You have had a suspiciously perfect start to life here. Perhaps Berlin can sense that it must go easy on you at first, that you are not yet battle-ready. Miraculously, you end up renting the very first flat that you view. It's on the first floor on a quiet street in the near east of the city; all warm wooden floors and buttermilk walls, it's your own small corner of honeycomb. Your landlady, a kind, softly-spoken knitwear designer, knows how hard it is for Africans to find places to rent here. She tells you the story of her three Moroccan friends with well-paying jobs who visited Berlin for a month, and who could barely get any apartment viewings in that time. I think, she says smiling, that my flat will be safe with you.

You feel safe here. It's not far from the centre of town, but your nearest train station is one which few people outside your area have heard of. You've only been here a few months, and to your delight you are already beginning to vanish.

***

Berlin Is Still Going Too Well.

Winter has arrived. The sky is sealed shut, closed until spring. The wind is a true Berliner; whenever it meets you in the street, it charges rudely past, convinced its destination is more important than yours. It whips through the city, hostile as a cocked pistol, barging through doors with the cold tucked under one arm.

Despite the weather's severe welcome, Berlin is still going too well. You have made several new friends. You are seeing a woman you met through the literature scene, and she gives you a happiness—a sense of calm, and comfort—that you didn't dare imagine. She believes in your writing. She is wonderful. You are told you often overcomplicate things when it comes to relationships, but this feels easy, so you allow yourself to enjoy it. You are not sure how things turned out so well—to be with someone so kind, so concerned about the world around them, so purposeful in their work. You float forwards, enveloped by love.

***

A Never-ending Blizzard Of Syllables.

There are many foods that have attracted your interest since you arrived in Germany, but the most intriguing of all these must be the schnitzel. You are fascinated by the schnitzel because it is not so much a meal as a thorough assault on the very concept of hunger itself. A thinnish slab of meat coated in breadcrumbs, it is a huge item, typically filling two-thirds of your plate. The largest one you have seen is not much smaller than a paving stone.

The schnitzel is Austrian but the Germans have adopted it with the vigour that the English have taken to curry. It is one of several immigrants to dinner tables in east Berlin, the more recent arrivals being Italian, Lebanese, Syrian, Colombian, Portuguese and Sudanese, but it stands apart from them in one crucial respect: it is generally consumed without the accompaniment of sauce. This is something you do not understand—this dish is biscuit-dry but many Germans eat it with no moisture other than a dash of lemon juice.

The startling dryness of schnitzel is in keeping with the Germans' apparently robust attitude to discomfort. When you first have a hangover in the city, you go looking for painkillers on Sunday morning, only to find that every chemist in your area is shut till tomorrow. It feels like a punishment for getting hammered. The next time you have a hangover, you have long since invested in painkillers—but then you find that they are not as strong as the ones you bought in Britain, and still leave you with a substantial ache, as if to make you suffer a little further for your drunkenness.

German bureaucracy makes you work for it too. You have learned to treat each new avalanche of admin as different stages of an assault course, at the end of which you will achieve integration in German society. The language sometimes seems like a neverending blizzard of syllables, even to someone who studied it at school. But slowly, gently, you make your way, dealing with the Künstlersozialkasse, acquiring your Anmeldungsbestätigung. Each month, you pass a new test; each month, the place you fled fades from view.

***

A Bath Of Stars.

There is a specific time and date you have been fearing for much of your adult life. When that moment passes, you will be precisely one second older than your father was when he died, and you will have precisely no idea what to do next.

When your father died, he was just eighteen days from his forty-first birthday. He was in a helicopter when it was brought down by surface-to-air fire shortly after take-off, and you have been carrying the weight of his death for much of your life. He was a refugee from conflict, but he returned to his country a few years later to fight for its future. He had a young family, and was therefore making the ultimate gamble. He lost it, and you have been haunted by that loss ever since. For the longest time, you have walked around with a deeply-held fear that you would somehow drop dead at the age of forty. You will never set foot inside a helicopter.

You haven't yet decided how you will spend that day, when you finally outlive him. Perhaps, you think, you might fly to Crete; which is about as close as you can get to the continent of your heritage, without actually going there. Setting foot upon the soil of Africa would be too traumatic. There, to mark this milestone, you'd planned to get a meal in a restaurant by the sea, and at the given hour raise your glass to the horizon. You've made it, you'd think.

In truth, you don't know what you'd think. You don't know what your father would make of the life you've made for yourself—whether he'd be proud. Though he has been dead since you were four, his opinion still matters. There hasn't been a year when it hasn't.

Though you're almost your father's age, you are still working so many things out. In some ways, he was so far ahead of you—he had four children by the time of his death, and currently you don't have any. They say that everyone's life is to be lived as their own, but it's hard enough just escaping the templates of your parents. You can't dodge comparisons—when you are tired, you even hold up your head with the same hand he did. Your mother asks why you do that. There is so much to worry about, you tell her, that your head feels heavy. She pauses, and replies, that is exactly what your father said.

You have often wondered what he would make of the life you have chosen, whether he would be proud of your direction. You can't say for sure, but you fear that he—one of the first black consultant surgeons in the UK, a prominent man in his community—might be underwhelmed. Because what are you? What have you achieved? You are a writer, making work that is far below his potential.

You have already chosen the restaurant in Crete, and the specific dish. It is a mix of meat and fish, a platter you had last time you visited the island. You will ask for the same wine you had last time too, a thick and fruity red, which you drank alone at a table at two a.m. as a group of locals danced by. What will you do once you outlive your father? You don't know—you can't know. That is why you will be eating heavily. You hope you will be drunk enough and full enough so that you won't need to think about it immediately, that you will make it back to your hotel room before you pass out. Or, better still, you will make it down to the top of the beach, where it will be late by then and you will sit with your knees tucked up to your chin and try to spot that point where the horizon meets the night. You know from the last time you were here that you will be unable to. Instead you will watch as the slowly-drifting sea perfectly reflects the skies overhead and the entire view becomes a bath of stars.

***

Running Through The Snow With Unicorns.

One winter evening, you'll go to football training with your friends, your local team whose nickname is The Unicorns. There'll only be about a dozen of you; the other thirteen members of your squad couldn't make it, giving excuses of varying quality. Some of them have had to work late, others have commitments to their family and their partners, and—you suspect—others still have been dissuaded by the cold. You saw the chill this morning, the frost leaving its palmprints across your kitchen windows, and you thought right then: yes, I'm definitely playing tonight.

Long before you first arrived in Berlin, you were warned about the winter. An Italian friend told you how she had arrived there one summer and survived just six months, the sun fleeing the country in late December and not returning till the last few days of spring had stumbled away. When some of your friends discuss the winter, they do so in quietly respectful, almost fearful tones, as if it were a mythical beast who might be trying to eavesdrop on their conversation. Are you ready for the Berlin winter? they ask you. With just enough swagger to hide your anxiety, you reply: Wrong question. Is the Berlin winter ready for me?

You promptly run out to buy a week's worth of thermal underwear.

They have often said that African footballers can't handle cold conditions—and, though strictly speaking you are British, you feel an urge to represent Uganda tonight. Your parents came from that country's northern region, and your grandfather coached its football team; somehow, thousands of miles from where he first took his players for training, you are paying an ancient homage. You put on your tattered national jersey, a black short-sleeved shirt with red and yellow trim and the badge bearing a crested crane, and you head out there. The few of you who make it to training are notably proud of yourselves, and the snow has the decency to wait until you have finished to flood the playing field. Within fifteen minutes of the final kick, the astroturf has been turned entirely white. You don't think your friends know what this laughter, this camaraderie means to you, and you can't tell them—not because it would make things awkward, but because it would interrupt this gorgeous moment.

A few days later you are talking with some friends and one of them mentions that they found it difficult to meet good people in Berlin. You think then of a story about your football team, and what they did one afternoon. One of the members of your team sent a group text message that he was having relationship trouble, and one of the others asked him to meet him at a particular bar within an hour. An hour later, the friend in distress was being comforted and consoled by three of his fellow players. You have seen many groups of female friends support each other like this, but not male ones; what is remarkable for men is routine for women. You wonder if it is Berlin that has enabled this, a city so stark in its challenges that it forces people to form unusually strong bonds. It could be this, but you have to give greater credit to your team's coach and captain. He truly understood that a football team is about much more than what happens on the pitch, that what matters most is everything before the first whistle blows.

***

Until You Have Fixed What Is Wrong With You.

Your partner shatters you, which is the only way she can guarantee you will not want her back. She returns from some time spent outside the city and casually asks if you are free for some food. You can't wait to see her, you arrange to meet at your favourite restaurant, you arrive and order some food, and then within fifteen minutes you are in tears.

The moment you sit down she starts on you. She tells you that her best friends do not like you, that her flatmate does not like you, that her siblings do not like you. Horrified, you ask if this means that she does not like you. She shrugs. You ask if this means she wants to break up with you. She says, if that is what you want. She cannot say it herself. She then leaves. Your pizza arrives and the waiter is kind enough not to make eye contact. You do not eat a single mouthful and you cannot bring yourself to enter that restaurant for another eighteen months.

You write to her and ask her why she has been so unkind, that until this week you had thought her one of the kindest people you had ever met. She then apologises, she thanks you for being supportive, that she got angry at being in a relationship, and she took that feeling of being trapped out on you. But you could have told me, you say, you could simply have said that you did not want to see me anymore. You did not have to do this. My door is always open to you, she says. I will always be your friend. But you do not respect me, you say. We never argued and then suddenly you acted as if you hated me. I do not hate you, she says.

You do not see each other for weeks and then by chance you run into each other at an arts event. There is a moment when you make eye contact and you both smile and then you both realise what has gone between you. It is the last time you will see each other. How are things with your partner, a friend asks a few days later. You tell her that she has broken up with you, but that phrase does not seem to do it justice.

You loved your former partner, which means that you have come to trust her opinion of you, and so you now believe her view that you are a terrible person. Given this verdict, you are afraid to inflict yourself on anyone else. You will stay single until you have fixed what is wrong with you.

***

How To Eat Cake In Berlin.

The best time to eat cake in Berlin is a weekday afternoon, say two p.m. on Thursday. You can't do it much earlier, because you won't have earned it. You have to get the timing just right—if you get to the café for three p.m. then when you finish you will emerge into a swarm of angry and homeward-bound commuters. The best place to eat cake—well, that varies. It depends what you are looking for. If you want to go somewhere where you can pass out after the arrival of the sugar rush, then there's that quiet spot in your neighbourhood, the one where the atmosphere is almost supernaturally gentle—where, even when it was full and busy one evening, you were still able to write a short story without being distracted. That's the same café which has a dog who seems to spend ninety-five percent of his time in a state of hibernation, slumped on a shelf just behind the bar, and who only wakes when another dog enters his realm. Then, he's almost on his hind legs with fury, and won't stop roaring until the door closes behind the startled and rapidly-retreating invader. That's also the café where the toddler babbles at you in Spanish and tries to impress you by holding up a series of nearby objects, waiting until you nod in approval before presenting a new one—a salt-shaker, a menu, a sugar bowl. You are always impressed. This place is as tranquil as your first girlfriend's bedroom at university, and when you fall asleep here no-one nudges you awake.

If you want to eat cake in a place where you can dream, then you wander down the street, to a café which also serves salty stew and cups of hot chocolate so thick you can almost stand a spoon up in them. This café is where you will spend many afternoon hours gazing out of the window and planning new adventures. It is the place where you are sitting where you heard from a dear friend for the last time, when he sent you a text message from his deathbed to remind you that, on that particular day, you were doing exactly what you were meant to be doing with your life: not worrying about making money, or what everyone else was achieving in their careers—just being. If you want to remember him, you go and eat there.

If you want to eat cake in a place that reminds you that love is possible, go to that café across town where they drown each slice of apple pie in whipped cream, that one whose back room is filled with Seventies-style sofas and which is graced with a small cabaret stage. In this café, over cake, love twice came close. Or, to feel similar, catch a tram fifteen minutes from your flat, where you spent a Sunday afternoon sharing Sachertorte on a first date with someone who understood you.

If you want cake for its own sake, which of course is reason enough, then go three stops down the line for a serving of marzipan-mohn, its thick, speckled layers of sponge dissolving the moment they touch your tongue. If you want cake which rewards your loyalty, then go to the cupcake store nearby, where every week you get a free helping because you are in there so often, and where you were just beginning to build up the courage to ask out the woman who you had seen working there for years and then she left her job.

To eat cake in Berlin properly, never reveal where you eat. If you must, then guard your preferred locations with the jealousy of an insecure lover. If you are feeling a little more generous, then leave hints as to where you have been eating, perhaps the odd photo on social media, so that the keenest detectives among your friends can figure it out. As ridiculous as it seems, not only to you but eventually your dentist, cake has become your sanctuary. It is your ritual. Each year, after you have completed your tax return, you catch the underground train to Mitte and mark the occasion with a dessert that costs no more than four euros, a restrained way to celebrate yet another twelve months as a freelancer. Cake punctuates your artistic career, each mouthful is a milestone. Whilst this town offers many escapes, many vices, yours is icing.

How To Deal With Heartbreak.

You're an expert on handling heartbreak by now—you could even publish an illustrated guide, like those ones they hand out just before take-off. "In the event that your relationship should crash-land, carefully stow your emotions over there. Brace for impact." The trick with heartbreak is to outrun it. Grief is slow. If you speed away from the scene quickly enough, the sadness may not catch up with you for weeks, even months.

You do what you always do. For the first ten days after the break-up, you make sure you're out each night. Not going wild with drink or any other substance, but hiding beneath dim lights and shrouds of bass-heavy sound. This is going to be fine, like it always is.

***

Life Keeps Dancing Forwards.

You are grateful that you live so close to a main road. For a city with so many long, wide avenues, Berlin is surprisingly like a labyrinth: if, one evening, you take just a few turns off a busy street, you find yourself in darkness and isolation. One summer, you were offered a lease on an apartment, but once you saw where it was you refused. It was four rows of roads away from the nearest train station, which itself was half a kilometre from the nearest strip of shops. You imagined coming back to that flat on a winter evening and you immediately and politely declined the offer, even though it would have secured your long-term accommodation here. You knew that if you had lived there, Berlin would have engulfed you.

When you're lonely, cities grow around you. It's as if each tremor of your grief makes them expand a little more, stretching every street you look down in either direction. You need to be within sight, if not sound, of frantic traffic—you need to see those blood cells rushing about their day, to remind you that life keeps dancing forwards.

***

Today, Berlin Punches You In The Stomach.

Today, Berlin punches you in the stomach.

It is one p.m., and you are walking back to your flat from a meeting. You've just left the train station, and are halfway across the bridge, when two white women approach you—the one on the left looks about nineteen, or twenty, the one on the right almost twice that. As they draw up to you, the younger girl playfully shoves her friend right into your path, so that you collide with her, lose your balance a little and almost hit the railing. You turn and look at the younger one, and she sneers, and you know.

What's your problem? you ask, but she laughs and walks off. Her friend, who seems much more socially awkward, joins her. Something in you snaps, and you think that you are not having this, so you walk up to them and ask again. What's your problem?

Do you speak German? Do you speak German? she says mockingly. Yes I do, you say. And I know you can speak English. So what's your problem?

I don't have a problem, she says, still in German. I speak German. This is Germany, I am from here.

There it is.

What's your problem with black people? you ask her. Are you a racist?

Yes, I am. So what? she says. I don't care. There are all kinds of racists. White racists, Turkish racists. So what?

Her friend stands between the two of you, and smirks something about you being dark-skinned. You continue to argue heatedly, walking towards the station, back in the direction where you have come. You aren't sure what you want to achieve, probably to retain some measure of dignity, and then you think you have to make some kind of record of this. They are just so brazen, so unashamed; and if you tell a story like this, without physical evidence, maybe no one will believe you. You take out your phone to take a photo of them, but the older one—you have to give her credit—has majestic reflexes, and snatches it from your hand. Sensing that she might run off with it—her train was just about to depart—you grab her by the other arm, and that's when a middle-aged white German couple, a man and a woman, walk over. Be calm, says the man, be calm, which is when you realise that you are not calm. This woman was racist towards me, you say, and I wanted to record it, and she's taken my phone.

Under German law, you can only take a photo of someone with their consent, says the man. It's probably the same in the UK, you say, calmer now, but I wanted to make a record of it.

Another man steps forward—black, early thirties, Seventies overcoat with high lapels.

I'm a police officer, he says. I have been watching all this unfold, right from the station steps. You, he says to the older woman, give his phone back. He'll delete the photo.

I didn't take one, you say. I wasn't able to.

She gives back your phone and gets onto the train with her sneering friend.

We can't solve this problem of racism by looking at these individual cases, says the middle-aged white man.

I'm sorry, said his wife. We're not all like that here. They get on the train.

You stand next to the police officer. You are shaking with rage—and, if you are honest, with sadness.

It's okay, brother, he says. You don't trust yourself to speak.

I'm from Congo, he says. Trust me, I know. I am from a small town in Germany, the things they used to shout at me in the street when growing up...Trust me. But it is getting better here.

I grew up in London, you say. London is fine but the UK is changing. I came here to get away from things like this. Christ, you sound hoarse.

I have been to London, he says. Germany is worse. But it is getting better.

They think we are animals, you say.
My God, the weariness in your voice.

Please, forget this, he says. Don't let this worry you.
I'm sorry, you say. I'm sorry. It's been a tough week.

These people are small, they are not educated, he says. We are stronger than them, my brother. Don't forget how strong you are.

Thank you, you say. Thank you. You exchange the firmest of handshakes, and then you walk home.

***

The Only Thing You Pray For, Even As You Avoid It.

Since becoming single again, your experience of online dating in Berlin has been a spectacular exercise in humility. Love has never felt so far away as it does here. That could partially be your fault. A few months ago a woman with whom you went on a date, who has now become a friend, told you that the first time she met you she sensed that, though you were single, you seemed unavailable. Yes—perhaps this was your fault. You have successfully navigated so many of life's challenges by yourself for so long that it no longer feels to you as though you need anyone else, and maybe that's how it comes across to others. Solitude seems to suit you so well these days.

But back to humility. There was a time when you thought all you had to do was be gentle, be presentable, keep doing interesting work, and you would meet someone who was right for you. But that was years ago. Now, you know that's not good enough. Increasingly, being single feels like some form of punishment. You wonder what is wrong with your heart, why it seems unable to connect with others.

Your desire for love is the closest that you come to religion. Intimacy is the only thing you pray for, even as you avoid it. Several people like you, friends tell you. But we aren't right for each other, you answer. How do you know, they ask. And you tell them: because you have tried. Out of desperation, out of the shameful agony of being alone, you have tried to date people to whom you were not attracted but who were kind, in the hope that love might develop, and that did not work. Instead, it left you each time with one friend less, and lonelier than before.

You have begun to withdraw into yourself again. Your bedroom is a kind, peaceful place—in a flat on a quiet street, with high white walls, a warm wooden floor. The first time you lay here, you found it the most forgiving of retreats. Few people have ever visited it. It has long been a joke among your friends that only the people you are dating ever get to see it, but even most of them never get this close.

***

You Wish Your Skin Were A Visa.

You wish your skin were a visa, since there are several places it cannot travel. It cannot go to certain European towns, because when it does it may be set upon by local youths, provoked by its confident passage down the middle of their streets. It cannot visit certain boardrooms, certain hearts. What a time to have a migrant body. What a time to live within this terrifying vehicle, this dark bulk.

What a time to be in this migrant body. When there are several of you in a particular train carriage in Hamburg, a cluster of dark-skinned men of African heritage, you begin to think: are there too many of us to make them comfortable? There are five of you, sitting in adjacent booths. Five! The other men are strangers but they have just boarded the same train and in their dress, Puffa jackets, oversized trousers and trainers, they are indistinguishable from you. Maybe if you dressed differently from these black men, the other people in the carriage would feel safer, that you were not part of a pack. Maybe you would feel safer, because you would not be seen as one of Them.

Look at the way you think about yourself now. African. Dark-skinned. Migrant. Fifteen years ago you were simply British, part of an apparently thriving whole. But now, with each passing year, your identity is being divided up, with each element progressively more dangerous.

Sometimes you forget you are in this migrant body and then the news reminds you. You are heading back to Berlin from Hamburg, tired but elated after a day of recording new music, when you see some troubling footage being shared on social media. A black man is lying on the street in one of Berlin's busiest districts and the police, instead of simply arresting him for whatever offence they have perceived, are striking him. You send a text to a friend, asking if they will meet you for a drink when you get back to town, and when you see them that evening you plead if you can spend the night at theirs, because you do not want to be alone in your flat just now: alone with thoughts of just how hated you are, in this migrant body.

***

Your Wardrobe Is Transformed.

Every time you travel away from Berlin, which is mostly for work, you feel as if you are taking time-out from the city. If you spend more than three straight months there, you begin to feel as if the place is absorbing you, slowly making you grey. You wanted that when you first got here, but you now realise that was a sense of desperation, your desire to drown in stone.

On one of your trips abroad, you decide that you need something to help you if not to survive Berlin then at least fight back against it. You wander into a fancy-dress store and see an item you would never have bought just a few years before—a gold and black jacket so absurdly bright that on a sunny day its glare would be uncomfortable to look at. It is far outside your budget, but you haggle it down to a price you can just about afford. It is unlike anything else you wear, which is currently a blend of blue and black, but it seems to suit you. This becomes your ritual over the next few months—every so often, to buy clothing with vivid colours, green, orange, red, turquoise—so that eventually your wardrobe is transformed. This is your daily way of marking your territory when surrounded by harsh terrain. This city doesn't compromise, so neither should you.

***

You Were Enough.

Your younger cousin visits Berlin for the day and she asks you to show her the city. So you meet her by surprise at the airport and you take her on a train, not to Kreuzberg or Neukölln or Prenzlauer Berg or Mitte, but all the way through to the western-most part of town to the end of the line, beyond the reach of soaring concrete or phone reception. You disembark at the edge of a lake and you sit there for a while, looking out over the town's border and across the water to the surrounding county of Brandenburg. I could stay here all day, says your cousin, in a state of wonder. You love surprising people who come to Berlin, who expect to hear the bass drum and end up entranced by birdsong. Some visitors cannot understand why you are at peace here, and you don't mind that, but you feel you need to explain it to the ones you love.

Your cousin's company is a joy and it reminds you how much you miss your family in Britain, especially since you don't have a relative living within a thousand kilometres of you. When you go to London you have dinner with several of them, in their early to late twenties, with their cars and their first jobs and even their mortgages, and you are so proud about how they have turned out. You can't tell them that, of course—

if you do, you will feel like their grandfather. They are just so kind and earnest and purposeful. One of them reminisces over how they first got into hip-hop—they put their ear to your bedroom door as you were playing a show you had taped from the radio, straining to hear which artists you were into, then quietly taking that information and building their tastes around it. You are astounded when you hear this—you never once heard their feet in the corridor.

You spend a lot of time thinking about trying to leave your mark on the wider world, but you rarely think about the effect you have had on those in your most intimate surroundings. Late one night, a relative calls you up to thank you for helping her through a difficult time. When your phone rings you are at your desk in the corner of your flat, the street silent, your empty screen gleaming and unimpressed at your attempts to write. As she speaks, your conversation reaching far into the early hours of the next morning, you slowly begin to understand that maybe the most important work you will ever do is the work you didn't notice, the type you did while you were running off somewhere obsessed with seeing your name on some imaginary bookshelf or festival billboard. It is the work of stopping and listening and caring, and you make a note not to get distracted from it too often in future.

You say goodbye to your cousin and as she heads home you are suddenly and deeply moved by the thought that you barely did any sightseeing—that she got on a plane in the certainty that she would have a great time hanging out with you. Maybe you should not be so surprised that Berlin, for all its beauty, is a sideshow: and that you were enough.

***

You Are Worth Being Known.

You are on your way to a date one evening, and just before the train pulls into the station you find yourself almost overcome with tears. You have long ago learned how to cry in public—you quickly tip your head back so that the tears don't run and swell the skin around your eyes. You plunge your face into your sleeves so that they absorb the water at once and so your eyes don't redden. Professional. You are crying because you are on a date with a very nice person and you have suddenly realised that you have nothing to offer her. If you ended up dating you could barely afford to travel anywhere with her. All you have to offer her is you, and you are worried that will not be enough. You have been single so long that you are beginning to think, or perhaps to see, that merely being yourself is not enough—because who wants to date an artist with potential. Because that's what you still feel like, an artist with potential. Someone who is surrounded by people who are truly doing it, who are making progress; someone whose plane is stuck on the runway while everyone else's took off a long time ago.

You get off the train and you are five minutes early for the date. Part of you is proud that you have even had the confidence to come out this evening. You gather yourself—*what if this person deserves a chance to get through your doubt. Don't make her fight to see you as you truly are.* You have a great night, in the end. The conversation is easy but not superficial, and the only thing really missing is that extra tell-tale level of physical chemistry. As you say goodbye, kissing her on both cheeks, it feels like a triumph. You did well even to get here, to sit in this bar as she approached and to think *no, don't cry, I am worth being known, I am worth being loved.*

***

Are You A Joke?

These days, doubt arrives with each dawn. You no longer need an alarm, since panic startles you awake. The doubt, my God, the doubt. And then there is the question you want to ask someone, but you don't know who. You want to ask someone who will give you the answer Yes, just so you will be free of the burden of always being the one to tell yourself. You want to ask them: do you think that I am a joke? Confused at first, they might ask—but what do you mean? And you will say it then: a joke. *Because I risked everything for a career that existed when I started out as a writer and now it doesn't exist at all. I thought if I wrote my very best work then I would end up getting paid well for it. Look at all the publications I have written for. I have done my very best. Fifteen years ago, someone with my résumé could afford a mortgage. But look at me. Every year I spend a month terrified at the size of my tax bill.*

You ask someone who likes you out for a drink but then you feel embarrassed. Perhaps they will be disappointed once they know more about you, that you find money hard to come by. Thankfully, a day before you are due to meet them, they have to postpone, and you never rearrange a date.

***

Too Old, Too British.

You started this year so well. You were eating well and sleeping well, cooking healthy food, reading widely and in great depth, playing a little sport, avoiding unnecessary conflict in your personal life and on social media. But then two things hit you in the same week. First, you sent some work to be reviewed by an editor and the news was as you expected—that it would need a significant edit before it would be ready. This confirmation causes you to despair. The worst thing about being a writer is the knowledge that much if not most of your work will go unpaid, unpublished or both. You don't know if you have the energy to plunge two more years into this project. Secondly, you sent some music to a record label to ask if they will work with you, and the rejection comes back that you are too old and you sound too British. You are devastated. You are most upset because the rejection is the same thing that you have been saying to yourself for the longest time—that you look and sound like a joke, and that there is now someone at a record label laughing at the thought that you might want to work with them.

Too old, too British. You don't mind your age, not of itself—but you do think that you should maybe be doing something more dignified with your life than performing. Stop jumping about on stage, and write, a relative told you recently. To your shame, you agree.

***

Berlin Is The True Ghost.

Most people you know who leave Berlin tend to do so quickly and quietly. It is only the minority who hold an evening of farewell drinks. Maybe that's due to the disappointment at things not having worked out, or the way that big cities leave you so thoroughly exhausted that you don't have the energy for any further ceremony. When people leave Berlin you often only find out through a photo from their new home on social media, or a telephone number that no longer works, a forlorn digital goodbye. You were like that when you left London, slinking away on a morning flight—you would have left without seeing anyone, had a dear friend not thrown a surprise party for you. That made sense to you, because leaving home was as devastating as a break-up.

Recently a friend has told you they have grown tired of Berlin, and you don't blame them. They never seemed to adjust to its staccato rhythms, its slow swirl followed by an angry thrash; never managed to navigate this warm rockpool filled with sleeping snakes. They are tired of the locals who growl where they should greet and of the friendships which never quite take root. You hope they have something to show for their time in this town. You hope they recognise their bravery in having attempted to make a life here. Before they leave, you meet them for coffee and you understand then that they were always wary of Berlin, that they never committed themselves to a city that in turn never really committed to them. For all the talk of people ignoring each other at the end of relationships, it's Berlin which is the true ghost, drawing you in with a flurry of wild promises, and then abruptly losing interest.

***

What To Do If They Don't Like It.

It is the question you have never easily been able to answer: what you will do if your work is met with contempt or indifference.

Even as you dream, you know you must plan for a nightmare. It is not unrealistic that you will create work which many people will either hate or regard with apathy. It is the pattern of your entire career.
A friend asks you how the new project is going. They look concerned, and so you decide to be honest with them—you tell them that you are preparing for failure, that you are expecting people not to like what you are making. That must be very draining, they say. Yes, it is, you reply, but this is just the way things go. You can never know how your work will be received and so you must enjoy making it for its own sake. There has to be at least one moment in the process when you sit back and look at the screen and think, yes, I have moulded this collection of words as well as I can. They may not be perfect, but this is the best I can do.

You must take your satisfaction wherever you can find it. If you knew the disappointment that awaited you at the completion of each new work, then you would never start anything. Please be kind to yourself. Remind yourself of the sign you have pinned above your desk: *You have a lot to offer.* On the page, and everywhere else.

***

Drink That Water.

You wake to the news that someone beloved on social media has taken their own life. You think about the walk you took the night before, when you wandered down to a local restaurant with the night so dark and your hooded head bowed so low that no-one could see your eyes brimming with tears and wondered how many of the nearby trees had branches that could bear the weight of your body. You thought it would be selfish to hang yourself outside your house but you could not help but imagine the feel of the scarf drawing itself close around your neck, the reassuring firmness of its grip—*I've got you, don't worry, I've got you*—as you made your descent.

You will never do this. You will never do this because you long ago promised two people, one to their face and one in your heart, that you would not take your own life. One was the first person you loved, and the other is a close relative who means more to you than anyone in this world. You made that pact and whenever your mind begins to drift in this direction you have to focus, you have to think of the first and most positive thing you need to do this morning, you need to keep moving forward. You don't really tell anyone this but a key reason you write is to save yourself—not in any spiritual way, but in the sense that any form of activity is better than slipping further into despair, and writing comes more naturally, if not more easily, to you than anything else.

You are not going to take your own life and you tell yourself that you are not even close to doing so. Reading the reactions to the stranger's death on social media, you are reminded how much sorrow it causes people when someone they care about passes away. You are in a place of hurt but you do not want to put others in that place too. Today you will do the things that seem embarrassingly simple and push onwards. File that invoice, dust down that surface, drink that water. And move.

***

A Pleasant And Unsettling View.

This year the sun has arrived earlier than you deserve. You need to earn the Berlin summer by struggling through the cold, but this winter has been abbreviated. It's only late February but out there it's bright, if not yet as warm, as an August morning. People are outside already, commuters and students, gleefully treating this premature heat as a welcome, not as a warning. And why shouldn't they? Who'd have thought that before March they'd get to wear one layer less? You are little different from them. You sit indoors, already planning your evening, knowing the temperature will be in the mid-teens. You're picking a jacket out, and then there's guilt at enjoying weather that shouldn't yet be yours, a climate shoplifted from another country. The building opposite the corner of your street faces the sun, and its vast adjacent wall offering you a long golden gaze. Rarely has such an unsettling view felt this pleasant.

***

Why Do You Keep Climbing?

You and your fellow artists are all climbing the same mountain. As you grapple with the gradient, your numb fingers clinging to the indifferent rock, some of them will race past you, up through the clouds, and beyond to the summit. You are rarely jealous of them, but you do feel envy. Because you just want to join them up there, and rest awhile, savouring the view.

What kind of a climber are you? Well, you're a slow one, sometimes a lazy one. But you are still there—and, though you perhaps set out with less equipment than you thought you would need, you are still ascending.

Why do you keep climbing? There are two reasons. The first is that there is little but pain where you rose from. If you look below, you don't see much but the hearts you broke, including your own. You see valleys filled with the happiness of others, happiness that could never look like your own.

When you were young, you kept having this daydream:

You and your friends, all children, were playing outside in a street of terraced houses, and one by one, as the evening drew in, they went inside. Soon you were the only person left, and it was only as you looked around that you realised you had no house of your own. Eventually, you gathered up a ball you saw bouncing nearby, and left that road. Perhaps, somewhere in the distance, there was the shadow of a mountain.

And the second reason you keep climbing: because every so often, just when you are about to falter and perhaps fall, one of your friends calls from beyond the clouds. Keep going, they say. Keep going. Maybe they could offer you rope, but you don't ask for it, not yet. For now, their encouragement is the only draw you need.

***

You Receive Your First Death Threat.

You receive your first death threat and you reflect that you did not know how hated you were until the arrival of the Internet. Now anyone anywhere in the world who despises you can find you. Their messages, sent with the fury and precision of long-range nuclear warheads, arrive at your various social media sites and explode upon sight. One of them describes how, should you continue to write about the subjects that you do, you will be murdered. Another is simply a selection of swastikas. A friend in another country drily informs you that your opinions are making the rounds, to some disapproval, in local fascist circles. One of your relatives sees your face as you look down at your phone to absorb some of this abuse and she tells you to log off for the day, seeing that whoever has contacted you has already ruined your week.

You remember the worst time they find you. You have written an article that has attracted the attention and the anger of a group of white supremacists in America, and forty-five minutes after you post it online the first of them gets in touch. He has a readership of hundreds of thousands, and has shared your work with his audience. His thoughts on your article are not particularly impassioned; he merely tosses it contemptuously to his followers, and their response is feral. They turn their rage upon you for three days. During that time, you sit mostly in your kitchen, barely leaving your flat, and though there are three doors between you and the outside world they have already broken and entered. Paralysed by the online onslaught, you can't look away from your screen. You wish that you had not written the article in the first place. You are alone and everyone you know has an office-based job, and so there is no one you can call during the day; so, for hours on end, you are surrounded by their taunts. You are back in the playground, beneath their deluge, maybe taking their insults because you think this is simply the cost of living life in the public eye.

You have got off lightly. Later a friend tells you that a popular far-right website discovered and shared her article on the same subject, with the result that she received death threats towards herself, her husband and her children. You have got off lightly: another friend is sent a photo of dismembered body parts inside a suitcase, the implication being that one day this could and should be her. You have got off lightly: another friend blocks thousands of social media accounts and every time she appears in the media she gets graphic descriptions of what men will do to her against her will. You have got off so lightly that you barely speak about the anger that is directed your way. You are also ashamed that you are upset by so little.

One time, when you are online, you draw fire for one of your opinions and you find yourself spending an hour ingesting the most acidic levels of spite from someone who cross-examines you on your social and academic background, and their interrogation, with dozens, possibly hundreds of people looking on, is so intense that you find yourself accounting for your entire life, even being goaded to describe how your father was killed, blown-up when you were aged just four. Your abuser relishes your discomfort, as do several of the onlookers. You know this because some of them share friends with you, and will continue to do so for years. On other days you are part of that audience of onlookers, and sometimes you send those being abused private messages of support, and sometimes you don't. This is just the way it is now, online; sooner or later, it is your turn to curse or be condemned.

***

The Deniable Date.

From your mid-twenties onwards, you have found that big cities specialise in one occasion: the deniable date. The deniable date is when you meet someone for a drink but neither of you ever actually admit that you are on a date: the benefit of this is that, if nothing romantic occurs as a result, then neither of you have to admit that this was ever the intention. The perfect time for a deniable date is a coffee, usually mid-afternoon, usually between freelancers. You will typically have met the previous week at a mutual friend's party, or after months of sharing idle jokes on social media. You're just catching up when you both happen to be free. You will be hoping that the person you are meeting looks as beautiful as they did to you when you saw them last week, either in real life or online. Your heart, for the briefest time, is wide open.

But there is a problem with the deniable date. Sometimes one of the two people will not entirely realise that this is an occasion with romantic possibility, and so they will remain oblivious to the efforts of the other. In such a case, the unaware person will be told of their pursuer's interest months or even years later *Oh, that guy,* a mutual friend will tell you, *he really fancied you.* You have been in both positions before, the coveted and the one doing the coveting. You wonder if that woman last year noticed how much you wanted her to like you, and you suspect that she politely ignored your interest.

Maybe the deniable date has become more common because, as you age, people become more defensive about the suggestion that they are looking for an intimate connection. This new world, the era of defensive dating, seems to suit you very well. You are a little like a football manager who sends his team to play in hostile territory, with the emphasis not on winning the opposition's affection but on making absolutely no emotional concessions.

This works for you very well indeed, until recently. You have just asked someone on a deniable date, for a coffee the following week. She doesn't seem to know that you like her—but does she know? You have met her once before so maybe there was not time enough for her to discern your interest. Maybe she thinks it is just a coffee? You have hidden your interest so well that it is probably invisible. Maybe she is hiding hers? You look forward to the coffee all week. The day before the coffee you write to arrange a time and place to meet and it turns out she has got the wrong day. What do you do then? Do you ask her to rearrange or simply be honest and tell her you are asking her on an actual date? She is lovely and you think you like her so of course you neither rearrange a date to meet nor tell her you are interested. Two weeks later, you barely remember how much you were looking forward to seeing her again.

***

Take Your Joy Where You Can.

Take your joy where you can in Berlin. Get that extra drink just before closing, always. You'll just about catch the last train and you haven't seen that close friend in months, so you owe it to each other. So what, you've missed the last train, the taxi will do. Relatively few people take taxis in this city—for those who do, it is a sign of bad planning and therefore of a very good night.

Take your joy where you can. Look out of the window of your evening tram, where the street lights greet you with high fives. As you walk to meet your friend in that bar, pay attention to the golden rule of drinking in Berlin, which is that on your way to meet a friend somewhere you will always see at least three places more lively and exciting than the place you are headed to.

Take your joy where you can. Take it all in. Enjoy that segment of the train journey where you go high over the river, a smooth marble path either side of the bridge, and then when your train curves to the right and then between the third storey of Kreuzberg apartments, ushering you slowly through the city like a child's fairground ride. Peer over the trees, rest your head against the carriage, and wonder how a mere piece of public transport can feel like home.

Take your joy where you can. Take pride in the fact that Berlin trains feel like home because they have the same interior as a suburban living room from the Seventies, as that floral-patterned oasis where you first learned to walk and soon after danced to Prince. Take pride in the fact that you now and then wear all black, the Berlin uniform, because when you're rushing somewhere it's the most defiantly lazy way to clothe yourself.

Take pride in the ramshackle. Savour that train ride home after the unexpected and unexpectedly lovely one-night stand. You know, that mid-afternoon journey back from some north-west district of Berlin, when you're leaning against the glass and your contentment goes bone-deep.

Take your joy where you can. Sit in that wine bar at the top of the hill with the long night ahead of you and stop right there, with the glass halfway to your mouth, and quietly celebrate. You've made it. You are not making it, you have actually made it—you have made it to this city, at this point in history. You have found this sanctuary, in amongst all the madness, you are paying your rent, and the work is somehow coming from somewhere and you are loved.

You and several locals have a joke. You notice that, most of the time when your old friends visit the city for a weekend, those ones you haven't caught up with in years, they end up not seeing you. They send you a series of emails and text messages just before they arrive, hoping you can find time for a coffee, maybe you can suggest a suitable place, and you don't hear from them until next Monday, if at all. Those who you do hear from will apologise, they will tell you that they got lost in Berlin—they will actually say that, each of them—and you begin to refer to them as *Lost In Berlins,* the specific type of person who upon setting foot in this town is overwhelmed with euphoria. You will laugh about it—a little bitterly at first, because you would have loved to see them—but you will understand. No mere urban sprawl, Berlin is a universe; if it doesn't engulf you on your first visit, you aren't doing it properly.

So take a lesson from your visiting friends, and get lost in Berlin. And linger. Take the hint. Look at the awkward structure of the roads and the way that the order of the street numbers is often impossible to understand, and take this hint: that Berlin may sometimes want you to suffer, but never to rush.

***

Denial Is Vital.

There are many days you wake when nothing else matters but this: the knowledge of what is coming. The climate crisis is arriving everywhere, far faster than you or many others thought, the only thing you don't know is how it will look. You are partly preparing for it by refusing to have children, although you have not told many people this. You have never been that keen on the idea of having a family, least of all now. You can't imagine bringing new life into such a world, into a civilisation that appears to be accelerating towards its finish, plunging headlong into a whirlpool of its own making.

You see so many people carry on as normal and sometimes you despair but then you think: what else are they supposed to do? These people have built lives at painstaking emotional and financial cost, and within the next twenty years the basis on which they have built it will be washed away. How can they—how can you—even imagine let alone exist with the reality of that? It is easier not to believe. It is too much to think that a displaced ocean could come and quite literally wash this all away. Denial is vital.

You are terrified, but it is only when you and your friends are drunk that you discuss your fear of climate change in full. One night, in the middle of a crowded dancefloor to the east of the city, you come across a human rights activist who you haven't seen in months, someone doing inspiring work in several different parts of the planet—the type whose social media account you read when your spirits are in need of a lift.

You greet your friend with a hug and though it is so loud you can only hear about half of her words—her distress is evident. She looks frantic and when you ask her what is wrong, she tells you that the environment is all going to hell, that it is too late, that she is just enjoying all these small moments of joy while she can.

You don't tell anyone else about this conversation because they will likely either not believe it happened or react with defensiveness and contempt. You also don't tell anyone else because you often feel like your friend. Months later, you will be making a similar confession, again far past midnight and far past the point of sobriety, when a friend asks you how life is going. You tell them that nothing else seems to matter but climate change, how you are glad you don't have kids, how you fear for your friends who do, how you fear for those kids to whom you are leaving this world, how you fear for yourself, how you most fear not having anyone else to share the coming years with, someone to comfort you and to hide while this unthinkable thing, this mass extinction, slowly rolls its horrifying way across the planet. Oh, says your friend. You are both British, so he wasn't expecting you to be so honest.

***

Berlin Is Not A Bubble.

Berlin is not a bubble. Many people will call it that, even those who should know better. It is not a bubble. A bubble is a carefully-sealed world whose occupants are oblivious to everything that happens beyond it. Berlin is something different. It is a refuge, an enclave, a safe haven. If Berlin were your bubble then that would mean you were incurious about whatever happened in other parts of the world. But you are acutely aware of those happenings, and that is why you are here. There is a very good chance that you are here because you fled the true bubbles of our societies—the small suburbs and villages where you were raised, where your difference was at best tolerated. There is a very good chance that those places, those bubbles, will resent how you see them now, that they will interpret your distance as elitism and snobbery as opposed to an essential act of self-protection. Those places, those bubbles, will not stop to think about what they did to you, that you were so traumatised that you had to flee at the earliest opportunity.

Berlin is not a bubble because that implies that there is some kind of protective force-field about this city, and there is not. Looking at history, looking at the Stolpersteine, those bronze plaques that mark the doorways Jews were abducted from, you can see that this city has not protected everyone.

***

We Exist.

You escape into sex whenever you can. It is the only place you can flee when the world feels unsafe. It is only there, in your bed or theirs sometime after midnight when the rattling fan whispers over your exhausted bodies, that you feel at peace. The people you sleep with mostly seem to want just the same as you: a few hours' break from the bleakness, where your fingers drift through the darkened room and over each other's skin, wandering in the direction of their sighs.

Your sex drive is often heightened by fear. You read of the murder of an African refugee, their remains found in the German countryside, and suddenly you are desperate for the warmth of another body. You suddenly crave being kissed and licked and held and overwhelmed, you lust after that frantic tangle of limbs at the bottom of which you are everything and nothing, beneath which you are their absolute focus and within which you can entirely disappear. There are people who will call you promiscuous but if they do so they will not understand you. You do not have sex to acquire but to remind yourself you are alive, one passionate moment at a time. One lover tells you that you are guarded during sex, that even when naked you are afraid. Days later, when you recall this conversation, your heart shudders so deeply that you fall back onto your bed, unable to rise for an hour or so, as if her words have eventually triggered an earthquake in you. You look out of the window at the cloudy sky, an egg-whisk of white and blue, and you remember the times you have made love in this flat, under the amber streetlights or the low glow of the bedside lamp, and you think of how fitting it is that they are called one-night stands; they truly are stands, acts of defiance, brief and no less glorious protests of passion, anxiety and grateful flesh, waging an intimate war against the brutal, encircling night. We are here, your bodies cry as they clasp hungrily together, we exist.

***

The Tactical Nap.

The most important arrival of your late thirties is the tactical nap. You are amazed at the sudden necessity of mid-afternoon sleep. Your friends laugh at your ability to fall asleep anywhere, and at a moment's notice—you attribute this skill to years spent at boarding school surrounded by similarly raucous boys, and then years one floor above one of East London's busiest roads. As a result, if you had a superpower it would be slumber.

The truly elite tactical napper can pass out on busy public transport, and you can spot a fellow professional the second they get on a long-distance coach or train. They are the ones who clamber on and dive straight for the seats directly next to the staircases, the ones where you can recline your seat fully with no-one complaining.

Maybe, as a side-hustle alongside your various creative projects, you can teach the art of tactical napping to new parents, or to people who have recently had traumatic break-ups. Workshops could take place on bus and train platforms on the way to work, and you could prepare helpful handouts about which clothing best enables swift sleep. Perhaps you could launch an app and sell it off after two years. If you're going to be exhausted this often, you may as well monetise it.

***

How To Walk Home In Berlin.

Years after your arrival in Berlin, you will still stop on your own street corner and take photos of your walk home, as awestruck as a tourist. That's because this city has a magic to it. You can find it in the soft streetlights curving low through the trees on an autumn evening. The neon fronts of the late-night stores line your path like landing lights. It's a scene as garish and joyful as the victory screen of an arcade game.

If you wish to take good photos of Berlin, then late summer afternoons are a must. Cross the Oberbaumbrüecke at five p.m., and watch the sun slip down alongside the Fernsehturm, the TV-tower, so that its glow folds itself around the building's edges. You'll try this hundreds of times on different days, but you'll never get the shot just right. That doesn't matter, though. The happiness lies in trying.

Best of all is the winter. Then, when it's two or three a.m. and you're returning from a night out, you'll take an extra twenty minutes or as long as you can before the cold starts cutting through your Puffa jacket: you'll take picture after picture of the snow-laden trees, their frosted branches glistening like a forest of antlers. You'll gasp at the beauty, time and again.

In many ways, despite its flaws, Berlin works—and maybe that is why its relatives are so ashamed of it. A place this unruly wasn't meant to be a success. Berlin is the queer kid who ends up as a happy adult. Your best friend will write to you on social media: *I think that you have a love affair with this city.* You smile, and you don't deny it.

***

And So You Keep Your Mouth Shut.

You fool. You have again said no to life-changing money. Even as you type this you feel a surge of pride that could easily just be vanity. How privileged you are to remain broke for the sake of your morals. You are strange with money. You only want to earn it if you feel absolutely justified in doing so. You will not write for betting companies. You will not take fees from companies involved in the exploitation of workers or from repressive governments. You are worried now because you refused thousands of euros a few months ago and now you are faced with payments you are afraid that you cannot meet, and again you wonder how someone given as many opportunities as you, someone who once studied as hard as you, is unable to earn the kind of sums that could make you financially comfortable.

It is the fear and humiliation of which you dare not speak, it is the quiet shame: that for all your visibility as a journalist, the money you earn from your writing may make your current lifestyle unsustainable. Your friend asks why you so rarely go on holiday, and you do not have the heart to tell him that you do not make enough cash to take more than a few days off. You look at your travel receipts from the previous year and you are astonished at how often you were on the move, on a coach here, on a plane there, mostly unpaid. You were exhausted. Sometimes the sums offered were so small that filing those invoices was more taxing than the work itself.

It is heartbreaking. One day you look at the five most successful articles you have ever written—not necessarily those which were widely shared, but those which contributed to the national or even global conversation, which shaped the debate in a positive fashion. You realise that the best paid of them brought you less than two hundred euros. You are proud to have written those articles, about colonialism and feminism and patriarchy and homophobia and immigration, but they brought you no financial security. You wonder if you will ever have a month where you are not terrified to look at your bank account, where you do not have to hold your wallet over the screen as you withdraw your money so you do not catch a glimpse of the balance which German banks insist on showing you whether you ask to see it or not.

You wonder what is wrong with you, with you and your stupid brain and your pompous morals. You wonder why you could not just take the money when that company approached you during the major football tournament to write a script for a feature-length documentary. You said no because the tournament was being hosted as a PR exercise by a murderous dictator, but you could truly have done with the money, and no one would have known you had taken it, except you.

But *you* would have known, and that is why you did not take it. This is happening more and more to you now. You are saying no to financial opportunities because you know that if you do take them then the resultant work, in some small way, will make the world a worse place. The problem is that you are always offered far more money for propaganda than for your own art, which you have recently begun to worry is not good enough.

You can't sleep tonight. Your heart is rattling as if you have just run for a bus. You can't think about anything but money and whether you will ever be a good enough artist for you to make any. You have begun to think that your moral purity will be the death of you. You can't stop thinking back over the last four years, to the two occasions where it looked like you might have commercially viable book projects about to go, and you walked away from them both. You refused one of them because it was a fiction project that might have refuelled stereotypes about black men. You refused the other because it was a non-fiction project that might have done more damage to the cause of feminism than good. You look back at those decisions now, which seemed so good at the time, and then you realise how difficult it must have been for your mother all those years, bringing children up by herself with no one to help her plot a course forwards.

It is then that you realise the worst part about being single as you get older. It is the choices that you make, specifically the bad ones. Stubborn, independent, insular, stuck in your ways, you take awful route after awful route, with no one to correct you. The most important thing for you in relationships has always been the companionship, the fact that you have a team-mate who will help you to fight your corner, but for the first time in your adult life you feel that you have blundered on alone for far too long, and you no longer know how to let someone in. As you understand this, you are in agony.

Your problems are insignificant compared to those you read and write about daily. You are not a refugee fleeing across several borders, you are not an activist in an authoritarian state, you are not living at the front line of climate collapse. No. You must live with the terrible truth that your discomfort is self-inflicted, that you are here in this state of financial precarity because you chose it. That is your punishment, to be endured silently, and so you keep your mouth shut.

It is a hard year for you, in a small way. You are finally reckoning with the long-term financial choices you have made. This year, some of your dearest friends are celebrating their fortieth birthdays back in London, and you cannot afford to go back and see them. You don't earn enough. At the age of forty, having travelled thousands of miles, having done hundreds of jobs, you cannot spend time with some of those you love most. There is not a week when you do not look in the hallway mirror and think, *my God, what have I done. What the hell have I done.*

***

You, The Gentrifier, Have Now Been Gentrified.

Berlin is a city which knows how to breathe. London doesn't—it has cluttered up its lungs with skyscrapers. Berlin has better airways, all low buildings and broad streets. One day you need to breathe more than usual and so you go out to the west, to the city's brink, to a lake called Wannsee. You go down to the uncluttered waterfront and look across to the surrounding state of Brandenburg, marvelling at how this town has tried to lie to you. Before you arrived, you had thought it was mostly hedonism, harsh architecture and partitions; now, you realise that Berlin is an introvert fiercely disguised as an extrovert.

Like many people, Berlin is making it up as it goes along, unsure whether to be friendly or fierce; here, you can find a smile wrapped inside the deepest scowl. Life here is recklessly improvised, a frantic jam session. If Berlin were music, then its innermost streets would be free jazz, a disorderly, jangling tangle of limbs; the districts of Zehlendorf and Steglitz would be a mournful piano score. Maybe, at each train station, the train's doors should open with a riff from the genre of music that best suited the area, the only problem being that you'd have to change the playlist every few months. By many accounts Prenzlauer Berg used to be trap, but now it's classical.

It's a little harder for you to breathe in the middle of the city these days. Just four years ago you had a favourite corner of a café that was never busy. Now it's almost always occupied, and in that time you've seen the price of the best meal on the menu rise from six euros to nine. You suspect that you virtually gentrified that meal by yourself—at one point you went in there nearly every week and ordered it, tender flakes of beef draped over a bed of relish and plantain, and your lust for it saw its cost soar. In fact, you can barely get a seat anywhere in there because they've been reserved hours in advance—this sanctuary, where you would once turn up and write for hours, making your way diligently through several cheap coffees and half of the dessert menu.

You, the gentrifier, have now been gentrified. What a shame that you gentrifiers have never met your ancestors, those people you pushed away to cheaper areas with your bigger income months or years before; once every ten years, you should have a reunion and bitterly reminisce, clutching your paper cups of Moscow mule and growling about how this town's landlords and businesses put cash before community. At the end of the evening you should stand in a long line, in the order that your spending powers evolved to claim the city; behind you will be Homo erectus, after you will be the tech bro. You hope he will have the decency to buy the drinks.

***

How To Handle Impostor Syndrome, Part One.

Here are some things you say to yourself weekly, sometimes daily:

- *You big, stupid, ugly fool.*
- *You are a joke.*
- *Look at the stupid choices you have made, that is why you are unloveable.*
- *You are a fucking embarrassment to your family, you are humiliating yourself.*

- *Look at the terrible choices you have made with money.*
- *Look how you have wasted your talent.*
- *The people who have come close enough to love you end up pitying you.*
- *If you are so gifted, then how come all your best ideas turn to shit.*

If you were good at self-help, you would do something dramatic and symbolic with the above sentences, like write them on a blank piece of paper, and then set fire to the paper. Then you would take another piece of blank paper, and write down every compliment your friends had given you in the last week: you would then make photocopies of that page of compliments, and pin them to the wall in different parts of your flat: one above your desk, one above your bathroom mirror, one above your kitchen table, one above the mirror next to your front door. If you were good at self-help you would remind yourself every day that you are a good person, that you are a kind person, that you have value.

You would keep reading these pieces of paper until you believed every word on them.

But you don't do that, because you are not good at self-help: you are merely resilient. And so you wait until you are overwhelmed with regret, then you plunge your face into your pillow, crying until your eyes are dry. Then you sleep, you wake, and you carry on.

***

You Are Finally Jealous.

You are finally jealous. You are shocked that you have finally abandoned yourself to this emotion, but here you are. Jealous, not merely envious: you not only want what someone else has, you resent them for having it. You are utterly disgusted with yourself—and, worse still, you are disappointed. You thought you were better than this. But how could you be better than this? As you approach your fortieth birthday, you look around you, and you are surrounded by people who have found others who will be intimate with them, who have spent years building lives with them. You wonder why you have not met anyone like that, or whether in your vanity you pushed them away or did not notice them at all.

You are so lonely that you feel your heart might burst. Why, you wonder, has no-one chosen you? You go home and you stand in front of the bathroom mirror at one a.m., having returned from a night out, and you are looking carefully at your face. Am I ugly? Is my skin too puffy and dark, do I have too much of a paunch? It is my fault, I am not in the best shape. Am I past my best, am I too old? These days, when people find you attractive, you find yourself feeling grateful that they would pay you such attention. You are so jaded at your lack of romantic success that you now doubt you would recognise the opportunity for love if it was presented to you.

Why do you always work so hard, friends ask. And you never have the heart to answer: because the harder I work the less time I have to think about being alone. But if you work so much you will never meet anyone, they say. Yes, you think. That has become the point of all this activity.

I think you have too idealistic a view of what love is, declares a friend. You want everything to be perfect, maybe if you had a more realistic view of it you would find it.

So you tell them what you think love is. You think that love is the small things. It is taking an hours-long Saturday afternoon walk by the lake with your partner and just listening. It is running them a warm bath and promising to them and to yourself that you will always be the very best person you can. Love is thinking ahead, being proactive about helping your partner to be happy—it is planning a surprise dinner for them the day they finish their exams six months from now. It is remaining grateful for them, it is continuing to thank them for the same things you did when you first met them.

Oh, says your friend.

I know what love is, you tell them gently. I would just like a chance at it.

***

A Successful Adventurer.

When the nuclear family explodes, Berlin is the fallout: it's the field that catches the first dust from the mushroom cloud. This city is an army of misfits, and maybe that's partially why you make friends so fast here: because people are in such a rush to build something better than that which they grew up in. Those of your friends who are very close to their families still seem to be the odd ones out—the only ones who have left their home towns or home countries. That's why their company is so exhilarating, because they each have the energy of a successful adventurer. Your friends are magnificent, and you believe that they are your reward for making the journey. In the squad of your local amateur football team alone, there are players who grew up in Argentina, Afghanistan, Australia, Brazil, Canada, France, Italy, Ireland, Spain, Turkey. It is something special to walk into a dressing room every week and be greeted by a group of the best human beings you have ever met.

You encountered these friends by chance. You were on social media one day and you saw that someone was working for an interesting start-up in Berlin, so you asked him if he would like to go for coffee. After getting on with him immediately, you ended up watching several football matches together in various pubs, and he then invited you for training with his team. As your new friend later tells you, the conversation between him and your new coach went like this:

Is he any good?

I don't know, said your new friend, but he talks a good game.

Your trial goes well and you are welcomed into the squad. You are not as quick as you once were and most of your team-mates are far better with the ball than you. In previous teams you had generally been one of the more gifted players, but here you are one of the least. For some reason, that makes you enjoy it all the more. After all, you reason, you are all in this team to build the same thing: and though you may not be the star architect, there is an equal value in laying bricks.

You love your new football team so much, and maybe you should get better at telling them. They are a galaxy of activists, artists, and simply good people. Maybe their positions correspond to their personalities; there is a scientist at centre back, an economist in defensive midfield, a chef at centre forward. Then there's you on the bench, an ageing striker, still a chancer, still looking for those two minutes in which they can save the day, steal the show, or both.

***

How To Handle Impostor Syndrome, Part Two.

You have found a solution—which may be temporary, it may be permanent, you don't know, but you will try it out. It is this: to tell yourself every morning:

> *Imagine what you would do if you were confident, and then do it.*

It is an excellent way to trick yourself into productivity. You contact a company to ask if they would like to work with you, you write to a producer and ask for a beat, you ask someone on a date. The company is keen, the producer politely declines, and the potential date says yes. But most importantly, you asked—you gave yourself a chance. You return home one evening and you see the signs on your hallway mirror, your kitchen wall. You have a lot to offer, they say. You can do it, they say. Yes I do, you think, and yes I can.

***

Your Ritual Of Closure.

It has been years since your first partner in Berlin broke up with you, and you decide that it is finally time to be done with that pain. As part of your ritual of closure, you go onto social media and you unblock her. The first photograph you see on her page was taken a year after the end of your relationship. It is a picture of her wedding, where she has just married someone who looks so similar to you that he could have been your first cousin. They got married somewhere in West Africa, and you wonder if they knew each other while you two were still dating, or if she ran away from Europe and found a happier version of herself.

To your surprise, there are tears, and then something even more startling happens: as you look out of the window and above the nearby building, you feel something snap back into the middle of your chest, as if someone has released an object that was attached to a length of elastic. You sleep for just over an hour, and when you wake all the pain has gone.

***

A Thin Film Of Dust.

The time has come for you to go to therapy. You know this because when you wake each morning your duvet feels as heavy against your ribs as a chest of drawers. Unable to move, you would happily lie there until your money ran out. The last time you consistently felt like this was the year after you left university; it was then that your ex-girlfriend told you that there would be days when just getting out of bed would be your greatest achievement.

You need to go to therapy: you know that because you have slowed down and you have seen nothing to encourage you to speed up again, and because in your flat there is now a thin film of dust on everything. Most people you know have not noticed this, because you are unhealthily good at pretending that you are still going at full velocity. But the signs are there, and you need to take note.

PART TWO:
Black Gravity

Depending on where Mohammed went in Berlin, his injuries
were different.
In Warschauer Strasse, on the bridge overlooking the train,
He sprained his left ankle;
As he walked in Treptower Park, he dislocated his right wrist;
In Spandau, he found himself convulsed with a stomach ulcer.
In other parts of the city, his wounds were more dramatic.
He avoided Sonnenallee,
Since three years ago,
Just by standing at a set of crossroads,
He'd broken his nose.
He stayed away, too, from Senefelderplatz, since that's where he'd
fractured his skull
The second he'd stepped out of the U-bahn.
No-one had been nearby that day;
It was as if he'd been attacked by the air.
Each *Kiez* of his town frowned upon him, it seemed.
His friends, amused then concerned by his never-ending series
of ailments,

Suggested he attend sessions with healers or seers,
Something to drive away the malignant spirits
That seemed to envelop him within the city limits.
Nothing worked, till he stumbled across the office of a black doctor,
A cheerful middle-aged man from Munich
Whose beard was the playful grey of ocean spray.
The doctor's diagnosis was bold, to say the least;
He said that Berlin had different weather for those of African heritage,
That's why its wind brought him wounds,
Why its rain raised bruises on his skin.

Though it was a view scorned by most medics,
Dr. Oppong had concluded that history was atmospheric,
That the air above a city carried the memory of brutalities past.
He believed, based on his extensive studies,
That racial oppression was just that: a form of pressure,
A physical force that stormed black people the second they left their
front doors,
A thing you could measure or sense, like temperature.
Dr. Oppong called it *black gravity;*
He told Mohammed that it varied in strength around Berlin,
Which was why some areas caused him more pain than others.
Black gravity, said Dr. Oppong,
Was strongest in surprising places;
Patients didn't just report suffering in Marzahn,
South Neukölln or Köpenick,
They spoke of leaving job interviews in Mitte with burst eardrums,

Of emerging from queues in Kreuzberg supermarkets with
punctured lungs.
Black gravity, discovered Dr. Oppong,
Was most severe on those weekends when the neo-Nazis marched;
The following Mondays,
Children would arrive at his surgery with fresh scars,
Wide welts under their eyes.
One afternoon, Dr. Oppong went with Mohammed to the site
Where the Berlin conference had taken place;
That forum of eighteen-eighty four,
Where parts of Africa had been handed out to attendees,
A whole continent pressed into gleeful palms.
Wear a thick jacket, advised Dr. Oppong,
And Mohammed soon knew why;
Since that afternoon, standing at that very site,
It felt as if their shoulders were pummelled by the clear sky,
As if slabs of stone had been thrown upon them from the roofs;
Their coats cushioned the blow,
Spared them the splintering of bone.
Various prestigious academic journals disparaged Dr. Oppong's views,
Said that black gravity was voodoo,
That weather-based injuries were a myth,
That you couldn't be wounded by a xenophobic mood.
Dr. Oppong sighed, folded away his notes,
And quietly remarked that he knew what he knew;
That wherever a right arm is extended and raised aloft,
The surrounding atmosphere cannot remain soft;
That trauma daily drifts up from the streets,

And exists in the mists and clouds around us.
In this way, history is forever among us,
Seething, teeming—
And maybe, if we heed its weight,
Even teaching.

No Voodoo, Then.

You have started therapy with Dr. Oppong, who was recommended to you by one of your oldest friends in Berlin. Dr. Oppong, born in Hamburg, now lives in the west of Berlin, which is probably as close a place as he could find to Hamburg this far to the east of Germany. He has large spectacles, round cheeks and a thoroughly grey beard, which together give him a reassuring air of kindness and wisdom. Your friend has told you that Dr. Oppong is especially good at talking about trauma, and, somewhat mysteriously, that he sometimes favours more traditional methods of healing, that he sees the world in a very different way. When you ask your friend what he means by that, he is particularly vague, saying only that if Dr. Oppong wants to tell you about that part of his work, he will tell you, but you absolutely cannot ask him. He is very reluctant to discuss it with those who are not open to it.

Okay, you say, this sounds weird. He sounds like a faith-healer.
For one thing, what's wrong with faith-healers, says your friend, don't mock what you don't know about. Secondly, I cannot recommend him more highly. He is an excellent therapist and he is just the right person to help you deal with what you are going through.

Yes, but the traditional healing stuff, you say, I am not sure about that. You don't need to be sure about it, says your friend, and if you are feeling that unsure about it I will pay for your first session. Since you are a little low on money that month, you accept.

You need not have worried. Dr. Oppong is wonderful. The moment you arrive in his apartment—all wooden floors and seats, in a quiet avenue a short walk from the station—it feels like your favourite aunt's living room.

He also knows when to let you talk, and when to interrupt, which he must do otherwise you would talk in one unending sentence for the entire session. You didn't realise how desperate you were to speak about everything that is inside you. When he wants to suggest something, he simply nods, and your mouth quickly decelerates, the years of unspoken pain shuddering to a halt at the end of your tongue. You tell him how you would like to work: that you could give him a long and complex family history, but that alone would take you six months. Instead, you say, you would like to meet each month and discuss the most intense thing you have felt all month, then work backwards from there.
Dr. Oppong says yes, that sounds good.

You talk and talk and talk until your time is almost done, with Dr. Oppong nudging your monologue this way and that. You tell him you are having what feels not like a mid-life crisis but an end-life crisis, that you often think you will drop dead before you pass your father's age, that you are not sure what you are going to do if you pass that age, that there are times when you hear your own voice on a recording that you feel like bursting into tears, because you have the same accent as the politicians who are tearing your country apart and you hope that when people listen to you they do not hear those politicians in you, that you are concerned there are places in your own town where you cannot walk after dark, places elsewhere in this country where you would be attacked on sight, places where—

Finally, with five minutes to go, he nods for a full five seconds, as if to bring an ultimate full stop to everything you have said. He then gives his assessment. Fear, he says, so much of what you do is characterised by fear. Fear of failing your father, fear of racism, fear of homophobia, fear of loneliness, fear of love. We are going to try to make you less afraid.

His words alone are a relief. Sometimes there is nothing more life-changing than hearing a diagnosis you already long knew from someone else.

What would you suggest that I do, you ask.

Take care of your private self, he says, treat yourself to your own company. Reduce your exposure to social media, staying on there too long seems to make you more anxious; the attacks from strangers, the anticipation of hatred. And stop trying to please everyone—there will be times when people will dislike you for doing what is right for you, and that is fine.

Later that evening your friend sends you a text, asking how it was to talk with the Doctor.
It was actually very good, you reply.
No voodoo then? says your friend.
No voodoo, you reply, unfortunately not.

***

The Hate Is Just Four Hours Away.

Four hours and five minutes: that's how long it will take for the hate to reach you. You have just seen the videos of the neo-Nazis on the march in east Germany, and you have been struck by one image in particular: the man with the large tattoo on the back of his neck. The tattoo bears the number 88, a numerical representation of *HH*, or *Heil Hitler.* At first you were startled to see it there, inked in a fat black font: that someone could be so committed to hatred to have it stamped upon their flesh for all time. And then you looked down at your dark skin, and you thought: *how long would it take for someone who hated me that much to find me?* And then you went to the Internet, to calculate the distance between where he was standing and where you were sitting, and you found the answer: four hours and five minutes. For him to reach you, to run upstairs and tear through the door of your flat, he would have to jump on a bus, then sprint 150 metres, then sit brooding on a train until it pulled into one of Berlin's main terminals. He would then make the rest of the journey on foot, presumably gaining in rage all the while, before seeing your monstrously foreign surname on the buzzer downstairs, sending him to a final level of fury. These migrants, he would think, coming here and taking our apartments, our jobs, our women.

Always their women. It is always, always their women. If he comes to your door, if he eventually enters your flat, there will not be enough time to tell him in your faltering German that the women of his country are quite safe from your advances, that in your considerable experience of the Berlin dating scene you are neither sufficiently handsome nor a skilled enough Lothario nor racially appealing enough to win their affections to any meaningful degree. *You are here to take our women*, he will accuse you, if he pauses before unleashing a possibly fatal level of violence. He might laugh if you are able to explain that you just came here for what you hoped would be a quieter life.

Four hours and five minutes. What can you do while he is on his way to you? That's barely enough time to organise and complete your first martial arts lesson. Maybe you can practise some of that free speech you are often told is so effective, and try to dissolve his bone-deep resentment through patient, logical and factually-rigorous discourse. Most practically, you can arrange to stay at a friend's place while you seek alternative accommodation either elsewhere in Berlin or abroad.

But you won't, though. Most realistically, you won't start practising Portuguese in preparation for a hopefully easier life in a warmer climate. You'll do what you always do whenever your skin colour feels like an existential threat: you'll release an exhausted sigh and carry on with life, even as the concerned white German friend you saw this afternoon is amazed that you haven't yet drowned in racism's rising water. Yes, of course it's worrying. But this is where you have made a promising new beginning, and you have work to do.

***

The Emptiness That Thrives Inside You.

All these things you do, says Dr. Oppong one day, this life you have. It must be lonely?

You think about this and you realise that even in your circle of friends, who are single most of the time, you are the one who is most often without a partner. This feels like a natural state to you and you wonder why that is. Perhaps you were prepared for it. You watched your mother, a war widow, bring up you and your siblings by herself, and maybe you simply assumed that this was how things worked. For years on end you have come home after a long day of elation and disappointment to find no-one waiting there.

You mention this to a couple of friends and they seem to understand you better than you do. But you're on a journey, one of them says. You were worried they would say something like that—that your endless quest for something undefined meant that you were never set for a conventional life, or even one where you ended up accompanied. You don't dare say this out loud—it is melancholy enough when you type it—but you hope that you arrive wherever that is before you die, you hope that you one day have that sense of home.

Or maybe this is your sense of home—this impermanence, this constant travel. Last night you caught the coach from Hamburg back to Berlin, after yet another day working on music—it was a three-and-a-half hour trip, long enough for you to disappear into either sleep or careful reflection and return again. There is a part of you that is happiest when looking out of the window of a fast-moving bus or train, gazing at the vast open fields that race alongside, marvelling and aching at the same emptiness that thrives inside you.

***

From Romance To Anthropology.

You know that your bisexuality will put people off but it never makes it any less painful when it happens. You will be told that the person in question was just not right for you but that's no consolation when you see a promising first date dissolve before your eyes. Oh, they say, the very second they understand you have dated both women and men, the tone of that single syllable so ominous. You know that in that moment your first date has gone from romance to anthropology, that they have gone from sitting with someone they could be fond of to someone they don't remotely understand. You are no longer an exciting mind and fresh, unexplored flesh, you have become a nervously examined object of curiosity. You sense that turning point every time and you loathe it all the more.

When do you tell them you're bisexual? There are no good answers. You can tell them on the dating site but if they have a negative perception of who you are then they won't even meet you. Or you can wait till you meet them in person and then hope that they'll take you at your word, that you're a gentle and attentive soul who won't go leaping into bed with any gender who offers the opportunity. There are no good answers.
At those times you envy heterosexual people, and homosexual people too. You envy the certainty with which they are regarded. You know

who you want, what you want, but the world often doesn't believe you—and, crucially, neither does the person opposite you on that first date.

It is briefly devastating and you have lost count of the lonely journeys home. Your only consolation is the glance you give yourself in the bathroom mirror at the end of the evening, the same look each time. The same glance that says, no, this is not a person who can travel the journey with you. But it's okay, it's okay. That person will come, they will come.

***

Celebrate Every Bill.

You haven't checked your bank balance in months, because you are scared of what you will or won't find there if you do. The longest you have gone without doing this is over a year, and you have long since learned that looking gives you an almost overwhelming sense of either relief or horror. It is best for you to avoid either extreme, and so you opt for ignorance. Sometimes your lack of money makes you ashamed—worst of all was that time when, three years into your artistic career, you went on a second date with a remarkable person and when the bill came the machine declined your card. Your date was wonderful—she paid for both of your meals, you are still friends. But the moment that machine hummed and sighed its disapproval—you will never forget it.

What a strange time this is. You could probably name the size of your readership on social media to the nearest ten digits but you couldn't name the amount in your bank account to the nearest thousand. That is because you are always waiting for that one job that will elevate you beyond financial worry, the day you will produce work of such singular brilliance that someone sitting somewhere will say, yes, here is a sum of money that will allow you to help with your family's healthcare bills and fund that solar energy project and put down that deposit and have something to offer to someone you want to share your life with.

You realise slowly, over time, that this is the wrong way to look at it, that you need to ease off, that you need to give your creativity more room to emerge. You cannot put so much pressure on your pen. You need to celebrate the small victories, the time you earned two hundred euros here, five hundred dollars there. You need to celebrate every bill you pay on time, and toast yourself with every invoice that you file. That's the only way.

***

Treat Your Loneliness As A Guest.

The loneliness comes about once a month, and when it does, it feels as if you've been winded by an invisible fist. It normally arrives mid-morning, on a weekday, about twenty-four hours after you last saw or spoke to another human being. It never seems to intrude upon you at an inconvenient time—not in a crowded bar of strangers, say, or just before bedtime. It always strikes you early, politely, giving you the rest of the day to deal with it.

You'll typically be at your desk when it comes, leaning over a keyboard in a state of gently rumbling despair. The blow will see you sink your head slightly further forwards, first out of pain, then out of recognition—ah, it's you again—and then of grief. Why the grief? Because you know that this is the monthly cost. This loneliness is the reward and the punishment for having escaped most of whatever you are running from. You'll never escape all of it, of course—you know that. There'll never be enough picnics under a fading Neukölln sun or laughter in a kindy-lit Kreuzberg backstreet bar to help you flee completely. This is as manageable as it will ever get.

But still—it's awful, isn't it? Even though this is the best you can do. It's either this or take that call from your siblings or try to rebuild bridges with your cousins, even though it'll be you paying for all of the materials and carrying out the vast bulk of the construction. So this is the loneliness and Berlin is the best place to face it, as well as evade it. Because Berlin is essentially the end of the world, at least as far as loneliness goes. This is the final stop on the train of solitude, the one where the conductor asks you all to change please, *bitte aussteigen*. There's nowhere you can go after this, nowhere more gentle, more brutal, no greater chaos, nowhere to be more gratefully anonymous.

Thank God for Berlin. Here you can sink yourself into equally lonely people, a night at a time; into their arms, their beds. Sometimes, if you welcome them enough, they will look around themselves, lower their voices, then take a tightly-balled handkerchief from one of their pockets, and slowly unfold it, showing you the glistening fragments within. Look, they will say. This is what was broken. Once they have done that, you will very likely never see them again. You carry your balled handkerchief too, deep within your stomach, and every month when the loneliness comes it feels as if the handkerchief has been stolen. You are grateful for the theft.

Sometimes you wish NASA would send you an email, offering you a one-way mission to some unfathomably far part of the cosmos. You'd take it at once, not posting a note on social media, but keeping an eye on Facebook, for vanity's sake. Even though you want to disappear, vanish beyond the night sky, you still desperately wish to be missed. When you finally arrive, the aliens will ask, *My God, what sadness brought you here?*

In happier moments, out in the street or on public transport, you look at smiling babies and toddlers with a state of wonder. They smile back, almost in bemusement—*why is that adult so happy?* You are happy because they've reminded you of something—that family life is something to be approached with joy, not fear. The babies gurgle in contentment and you grin with embarrassment because just then you felt like gurgling too.

Back in your flat you assess what to do with your loneliness. You wondered if it was medical, if it might be depression, and so you go to ask Dr. Oppong. Oh, no, it's nothing like that, he replies. We can give you something for depression. This—it's just *Fluchtsteuer.* Escape tax? you ask.

How do I get a refund? You don't, says Dr. Oppong. Well, not unless you go back in the direction you came from. It's just the price of any kind of physical and emotional freedom. But if I am still paying it then I can't be free? And then Dr. Oppong, in that voice—always in that voice, like he's telling you the end of a fable—ah, but you can't truly understand freedom without captivity. Then he pauses—because he doesn't want to make light of your suffering—and says: but seriously. When the loneliness comes, welcome it. By coming to you in a quiet moment, it is honouring you. Don't distract yourself from it—treat it as you would treat a dear friend who has travelled many miles to reach you.

And so, back at your flat, this is what you do when the loneliness comes. You step away from your desk and you pull up the blinds, allowing just enough natural light to pass through, enough to soothe you when you wake from what you're about to do. And you lie on your bed, on your side, never on your back, and you tuck a pillow into your stomach, wrapping yourself around it. You sink your face into another pillow, and there you cry, softly at first, as if warming up, and then you sink your teeth into the pillow's friendly flesh and here they come, the giant shuddering sobs, and finally you open your mouth to wail, the pillow swallowing it, saltwater and all; and then you sleep, you sleep, you sleep.

***

In The End, It Was All About Love.

There are only two states where you have ever felt safe: when you had money and when you had love, and you have never really had much of either. The lack of money—that is your fault, your choice: you could have had a stable career, but instead you chose to make your way as an artist. Or did you choose it? Some tell you that the road chose you.

And the lack of love: maybe that is your fault too, maybe it is also your choice. Because there are people who have tried to love you, but you have not allowed them to do so.

Maybe you are being unfair on yourself here. You have dated people whom you did not find attractive but who had a beautiful warmth of spirit, and you tried to make it work with them, you really did, but you ended up as friends. And there were others, the ones who were wonderful but who wanted kids but you didn't.

You are amazed at how quickly and easily people around you start families. You marvel at their confidence in building something that may long outlive them. At weddings, where you are frequently one of the few single people there, you increasingly feel like an alien. You look at married couples in awe. Who are these extraordinary human beings, who have convinced other human beings to make such significant emotional investments in them?

You are glad you do not have a child. You couldn't imagine looking at them across the breakfast table, and risking eye contact—the eye contact which, within a split-second, would reveal to them the most horrifying of all truths: *Daddy doesn't have a clue what he is doing.*

You fall in love, or at least you initially think you do. Looking back over it, you didn't fall in love, you fell in safety. You enjoyed dating someone who was gentle and didn't hate you, but it wasn't love. You know what love is, and you haven't felt that in years.

Several people have a theory as to why you are single, including you. Some people say it is because you are looking too hard for it. Some people say it is because you are not looking at all. No one, including you, ever tells you that it is just bad luck.

You think that you are single because you are difficult to love. That might well be true. What is certainly true is that it has been so long since you have been in love that you have begun to think that it may never happen again, and that thought is exhausting. You don't know how single parents do it.

You look at the empty laptop screen before you and the list of new projects next to it, and you can't be bothered to start. *What is the point,* you think, *of all this writing, all this creating, if at the end there is no-one to stroke your head on the night bus home, no-one's hand to hold in a darkened cinema, no-one to feed ice cream on the sofa on a Sunday afternoon. What is the point of trying to put joy into the world when you can find none of your own.* You think of those comedians and soul singers who entertained and brought solace to so many but who never met someone who cherished them; and then you look around your flat, where barely a friend or lover ever sets foot, and you realise that, though oceans away from their success, you are still sailing in similar waters. What is the point of all this, you wonder; and then, because you have rowed so far out into this life that it feels you have no other options, you start to type. *In The End*, you begin, *It Was All About Love.*

***

How To Play The Race Card, In Twelve Simple Steps.

If you must insist on being a dark-skinned black male in a major continental European city—let's say, Berlin—then here—assuming that you intend to make your life a little easier—is how you go about it. Here, in a short, simple twelve-step programme, is How To Play The Race Card:

1. Make sure there aren't too many of you living in your apartment block. Any more than two is officially an infestation. Make sure there are not too many exotic emissions from your flat. Ethnic smells are fine—ethnic sounds and ethnic people are not. Outside, when approaching a local, make sure you greet them in their own language as soon as you are within earshot. Integration!

2. When going through Customs, don't look too cocky. You'll get stop-searched if you look too free, if you're too gleefully crossing borders. So what if you're going on holiday? Suck it up—quell that smile. Halt that swagger. The recommended facial expression, when you encounter immigration officials, is that of a dog taking its final walk—you must look utterly world-weary, careworn, whilst taking care not to avoid eye contact, lest you appear shifty. Remember: visibly broken souls do not smuggle drugs.

3. Promptly follow every public criticism of the country where you now live with a phrase containing gratitude. For example: ***That Nazi march was terrifying but the schnitzel here is nice.***

4. If you are sitting on a crowded train yet everyone refuses to sit next to you, take advantage of the resultant space. Make a show of it. Manspread. Take a photo of the space and post it on social media, as an example of the Black Gap, the mystical force-field that often seems to appear around post-puberty black men in public. Save the photo on your phone and joke to yourself that you'll save it for your grandchildren, you'll enhance it with a sepia filter and you'll all laugh at how toxic the times were back then. ***Granddad, they must have thought you were an animal!*** Reflect on whether you smell—look, it is possible. It could be that fellow passengers are utterly repelled by your smell. Later that evening, when you get to your partner's flat for dinner, don't tell them that a Black Gap appeared on the train next to you for the second time that week. Not until dessert is served, at least. You don't want to ruin the mood.

5. Each morning, before you leave the house, remind yourself that you aren't ugly. Stare in the mirror and try to feel handsome before you head out of the door. Having a shave often helps—smooth skin feels more attractive. Stubble is for drunken men who have abandoned hope. For the smoothest skin, apply baby oil to your face immediately after a shower, then pat it dry. Don't leave the flat before you feel handsome. There will be days when you don't leave the flat.

6. Don't leave the flat. Remember that time you saw the bus driver wearing the neo-Nazi dress code, the Thor Steinar baseball cap. Remember the time you were racially abused by two white

women at the top of your road. Remember when they put their hands on you—they actually touched you. Don't leave the flat.

7. Get on a plane to another country as if to escape but then come back because you understand that all you ever get wherever you travel is merely different flavours of racism, that the seasoning may be different but ultimately the meal remains the same.

8. Don't laugh it off. Don't make a quick quip when the Turkish kids in the local park ask if they can see your huge cock. Don't joke about your big dick. Don't laugh it off.

9. If you laugh it off that tells people it is fine, and it is not fine—you are not fine. Remember that you have seen other black people arrive in, and then leave, this country, exhausted at being treated so poorly. Ask yourself the simple question—do you have unfinished business here. If the answer is yes, then stay. If the answer is no, then run, my God, run, you are not a fucking martyr.

10. For the sake of sheer survival, focus upon the positive. There are people who love you. Many people who love you. Rhea, Sasha, Burçu, Gerdi, Alex, Andrew, Josh, Lee, Ryan, Krisz, Steffi, Soja, Jonathan, Jessica, Jennifer. Look at the joy with which you are greeted at the local supermarket, at your favourite restaurant. Brother, they call you. The Lebanese, the Vietnamese, the Sudanese embrace you. Many people, many fellow non-white immigrants love you.

11. Remember that no matter how much you might feel despised or stereotyped, you are only ever one new conversation or great first date away from changing your life. Cherish your friendships. Send text messages out of the blue to those who are dearest to you, telling them you love them. When they ask ***whatever prompted that?***, then tell them ***I am grateful for you, and whenever I feel grateful for someone, I tell them.***

12. And finally, step number 12. Start wearing brighter colours. Pink, green, red, yellow, orange, even gold. Shine so that you are undeniable. Your skin is a spectacular canvas. Each time you are smiling and vibrant in a place that would rather see you dull and invisible, you will grow in hope. Keep loving, keep pushing. Keep loving, keep pushing. Keep loving, keep pushing.

***

Freedom Of Movement.

You don't tell Dr. Oppong about your dream. You are getting on with him so well in your therapy sessions that you don't wish to spoil the mood. Dr. Oppong reminds you of your favourite uncle, the one who fled a war in Uganda and who is now living out his days in Scandinavia. Every time you see that uncle, he asks politely and warmly after your well-being, about whether you have met someone nice. Your monthly visits to Dr. Oppong's office have started to feel similar—he is becoming a family member you don't want to disappoint, whom you want to show that you are making progress in your grand German adventure.

And that's why you don't tell him about your dream.

The dream. It's you and two black male friends, walking down the middle of a Berlin street one autumn evening. It's eight p.m. but such is the quiet that it may as well be midnight; it's that time of day when the nearby bars have already absorbed most of the locals. The branches of the trees reach across the road towards each other, joining hands and forming an archway above you. Moonlight pours over the cobblestones like milk. You're all so happy. You're on your way to see a friend's DJ set at a bar in Revaler Strasse, and your German is good enough that the bouncer won't turn you away at the door. Are you visiting Berlin for the weekend, he'll ask you. No, I'm a local, you'll reply, *ich wohne um die Ecke, nur zehn minuten zu Fuss.* He'll smile at how offhand you are and then he'll let you into that space, that womb of soft light and warm sound, and you'll sway there till the middle of next morning.

But you and your friends will not get that far. You have reached the end of the road, and the archway of trees has been replaced by a metal one, just before a small staircase that leads down into a courtyard towards the bar. Either side of the archway are two black men, just as dark as you, not as free as you; they are there so the white tourists who want weed can easily find them. They are trying to warn you not to go through the archway, but you don't listen. One of them says something in a language you don't understand but the fear in his voice translates it for you. When a black man is afraid the language is universal. Brothers, please. Do not enter. You don't listen to him and you are angry at yourself even for making eye contact, for entertaining his doubt. We are trying to help you. One of them grabs the sleeve of your hoodie and for a moment he holds you. He is wearing a hoodie too, his is black whilst yours is bright red, and a passing policeman could not have told you apart. The only thing separating you is the colour of your passport, which sits between you like the width of an ocean.

Come on, says one of your friends. They are visiting you from London, and they are impatient to get on with their night. One of them has already gone through the archway, and though he has only gone a few yards you can no longer see him. Come on, he says again. He doesn't like the fact that the drug dealer is touching you, and he pulls you by the other sleeve. The black man by the door lets go. Brother, please, he says. It is this animal. Wherever the trouble happens, we see it. He points to a small silver image stencilled on the brick wall next to the archway; through this gloom, it looks like a hook. We cannot remove it. Come on, says your friend for the final time, and yanks you through the archway.

Ten metres ahead of the pair of you, your friend is lying dead on the poorly-lit floor. He is on his front and you can't see his face but you know he is gone; because when death visits any place then everything in that same area is drawn towards it like a vacuum, and right now you are sensing that familiar, dreadful pull, like someone tugging at your vest. Your other friend runs forward and drops to his knees beside the body. You are just about to join him when, swinging in somewhere from your left, a baseball bat leaves a deep dent in the back of his head.

Your chest feels as if it has been torn in half, and you look at the man who swung the bat. At first you could see only your two dead friends but now you can see him and five other white men, standing in a wide semi-circle, facing you. You are not standing outside a courtyard in Berlin anymore. You are in the centre of what seems to be a warehouse, somewhere above street level. It is late here too. There is a single light in this room, set in the ceiling above the distant door, which falls over the shoulders of the men and just short of the wall behind you. There is only one exit. The men are smiling. Each of them are holding baseball bats, whose surfaces are busy with blood. On the right cheek of the man who swung the bat, you see the same symbol you saw on the side of the archway.

You can see every detail now, as you surely do before you are about to die. Most of the men are a similar height to you, and are wearing black tracksuits, black trainers; they are slim but athletic, their calf muscles pulsing against the inside of their trousers. Their shoulders rise with excitement. You can tell that they have hunted before.

The man with the silver hook on his face looks like he is five years older than you, but the others are young enough that they could easily be his nephews. He is in superb shape, he would turn envious heads in any gym. The others are waiting for his instruction, his voice will be the starter pistol. Your mouth tastes like that time as a child when you put an old coin under your tongue. You would scream but even the stars seem closer than anyone who could help you. You look to your left, towards the long, thin windows, and see the trees gathered outside. Before the leader can speak, before he can swing, you are sprinting towards the window, pulling the hood over your head, turning your left shoulder towards the waiting face of the glass, and just before impact you jump.

The glass bathes you like rainfall, and as you soar the trees reach out to you. Autumn hasn't stripped them yet, and at first their bustling branches ruffle your head like adoring aunts. You reach desperately for any kind of hold, grasping with your arms and thrashing with your legs, but now the trees show you tougher love, pounding you between them and downwards, handing you roughly down to the bushes below.

You roll out from the shrubbery and the pavement is a cool palm against your cheek. Two floors above, you hear the yells of the angry men, their voices disappearing towards the staircase. Your body is a mosaic of bruises, the pain is patiently waiting to arrive. You draw yourself to your feet and you look either side of you. There is a warehouse opposite you, its lights long dead. To your right there are the impossibly high walls of a car park. To your left—to your left, lined by orange streetlights, welcoming as a runway, there is the open road. You run. My God, you run.

By the time you are at the top of the road, a hundred metres away, the men have reached the street. They are chanting. Wherever you go in the world, these three words, travelling at the speed of hate, will always seem to catch up with you: run, nigger, run. The road curves to the right, and is now parallel to the motorway, a few metres below you. You think of running out into the middle of it, perhaps flagging a car down, but there are no vehicles in sight, not yet. All you can see is the stars and the trees. The men are moving closer and so is the pain from your fall. There is, thank God, a motorway service station ahead, about one hundred and fifty metres from you—the store is still open, there is a single white lorry parked outside—as you approach, your legs tumbling down the shallow hillside and into the car park, the lorry's engine opens its lungs, its front wheels twist towards the motorway, please, please wait, but the driver can't hear you, and the lorry picks up speed, the first of the chasing men is close enough to make a grab for you, and he has dropped his bat long ago, because he wants to truly claw at you, hook his fingers into your flesh, and you find a final lurch of acceleration, God knows where from, you are now the only thing faster than hate, which is the speed of a fleeing refugee—and you leap, you clutch one of the poles on the back of the lorry door, you scramble onto the shallow step, and as the men thrash their bats against the ground the lorry carries you out with it, onto the motorway, away beneath the gentle valley of stars.

This is your dream, and when it recedes you are sitting in front of Dr. Oppong. He has been watching you, concerned, for how long you don't know. He asks whether you feel safe in Germany. You hesitate; and by the time you speak something, you have already answered.

***

You Feel Safest When Adjacent To Danger.

You have stopped online dating. Just before you did so, you had accounts on three different websites, none of which yielded anyone who you connected with. Maybe the problem is you, maybe it isn't, but the one thing you do know is that it has begun to feel unpleasant to be reminded constantly of your inability to meet someone you would like to date. Online dating has done little for you other than magnify a loneliness that for long periods you were so busy that you barely noticed. From now on, for you, meeting people must be spontaneous.

A friend asks you if you actually want a partner and you hesitate. You have spent so much time thinking about what it would be like to be with someone and no time at all thinking about whether you should. After all, you are so comfortable in solitude. Nothing makes you happier than sitting in the corner of your favourite café on a late winter evening, a glass of Glühwein in your left hand and a gaping paperback in your lap. That's where you're most at peace; looking up from your book now and then, having come to the end of a particularly elegant or spellbinding paragraph, to see the bare branches twisting slowly in the breeze. For you, that's always been happiness; snatching a moment of calm and warmth whilst the shadows lie in wait.

Sometimes you wonder if you could ever be happy in a place where you didn't have to fight for your joy. Another friend tells you that you always seem to do things the hard way, to find the most aggressive way to test yourself. But it's not that you treat comfort with contempt, it's just that you have long learned not to trust it. The worst things that have ever happened to you or your friends emerged from serene summer afternoons, from clear blue skies. Maybe that's why you now feel safest when adjacent to danger.

***

Happiest In Transition.

There are so many photos on your phone of this city. You take them every time you feel supremely happy. Most of them capture early evening strolls to meet friends for drinks, either along narrow streets where the trees rise almost as high as the buildings or vast avenues where the sun awaits you at the end. Here's that time you went to see that director of a human rights organisation for a few too many glasses of white wine, here's that time three of you went to welcome a friend back from four months abroad. Every hug was ecstatic. Did you ever feel tempted to stay there, to leave Berlin, you ask. He just smiles. A few months ago, your cousin affectionately called you a hippy, and it's one of the kindest things someone has ever said to you. You are probably happiest in transition, in that space between completing a satisfying piece of writing at your desk and heading out to embrace both your loved ones and the long night ahead. On those half-hour journeys—because everywhere in Berlin is half an hour away, that's the rule—you wander along and keep reminding yourself how lucky you are, that this is the best life gets, between the temporary rest of your ambition and the promise of open arms.

***

Voodoo, This Time.

You have decided that this will be your last session with Dr. Oppong. He knows this already, he says he could tell that from your previous visit. How come, you ask. You were not as open as you normally are, he says. It seemed as though you were getting ready for something else.

Well, yes, you say, but it is nothing personal. I am very happy with the work we have done together, you have helped me so much.

Dr. Oppong frowns. Perhaps you fear I have become too familiar?

No, not at all, you say. Just that I have something very significant coming up. My mother wants me to visit my father's village for the first time in thirty-five years—I didn't want to go at first but now I think I will. At first I was kind of doing it for her but now I have decided to do it for me. I think—that's kind of the next stage. That I need a clean break with everything.

You are hoping to find answers there?
I don't know. Closure, I hope.

That sounds wise, says Dr. Oppong. In any case, it has been a real pleasure working with you. This has been—and I know you don't like this word—a journey.

No, I don't like it, you say, but you smile.

I would only say that, whatever you do next—please remember that there will always be a next thing, another goal to reach. Another excuse not to like yourself until you have achieved some new ambition. But it's okay to like yourself right now, though. It's okay.

His words almost wind you and you don't speak for a moment because you don't trust yourself, you are afraid the tears might reach your eyes quicker than the speech leaves your mouth.

Dr. Oppong, I am so tired of giving up on myself.
Then don't, he says gently. Then don't.

You want to hug him but it doesn't feel right. Instead you nod to thank him for his help, hand him the money for the final session, and turn towards the door.

I must apologise, too, says Dr. Oppong, as you walk out into the stairwell, and his tone is notably mournful. I did become too familiar. I don't mind doing what I did for you, I will keep doing it, but I can no longer do so whilst you are my client.

What do you mean, you ask, already halfway down the staircase. Dr. Oppong is resting against the doorframe, with a strange mix of pride and sadness drifting across his face.

Your dream, he says, the one where you are being chased through the night, and you are rescued by a lorry. The person driving the lorry, he says, it was me. It will always be me.

Before you can ask anything, Dr. Oppong has closed the door; like one of his long nods, it feels like the end of your conversation.

On your walk home, you text your friend. Just had my last session with Dr. Oppong, you write, it was weird. But good weird. Great in fact. If that makes sense?

He was the lorry driver, wasn't he.

Wait what?

Haha, not to worry, I'll explain soon. Let's grab a beer when you're back from Uganda, okay? It's not one for a phone call.

Yeah, let's. Sorry—sorry. This is still sinking in.

Yeah it's a shock to everyone at first.

Everyone?

You heard me! Chat soon mate.

Ha, okay, for sure. Chat soon.

Then a couple of minutes later, since your friend can't resist:

Voodoo this time, then?

Yes, you reply. Voodoo, this time.

PART THREE:
Your Passport

I have your passport.
What more could I ask for?
From its few clues, I can soon deduce
Who you were, how much further in your pursuit
That I have to go, for it's natural
That a son plays catch-up, that's his role;
Yes, that's his role...
...So; Dad, you came from Uganda
Born in its Northeast in the early Forties...
It's clear from the cluster of stamps in here
You loved Kenya, Zambia, Tanzania—
You loved travelling,
Dressed sharp as a javelin,
Your handwriting was sleek...yes, I see comparisons;
Even your jackets I wear as well,
Those Seventies classics that they rarely sell—
And look! I outgrew you, I six-foot-twoed you,
Touché, you lose, at six-foot-one;
And as for professions, we've different ones...

Didn't mimic you as a medic—I loathe blood—
But I've opened more wounds than you ever closed up,
Sewed up, since we poets, we bare souls
More urgently than you surgeons repair souls...
...It says here you were born five days from Christmas;
I used to own your leather-bound book of Scriptures
But to my mother, that's now been restored
For my rapport with the Lord isn't as warm as yours...
...Speaking of Mother, given you're her husband
You'd think she'd mention you loads, but she doesn't;
I guess she's still upset that you went to war
But when she talks of you, there's an impressive warmth:
He was the best man, you can rest assured;
Didn't think that the fist was the best resort;
Only thing, I confess, that I'm left to mourn
Is that he walked in the steps of the less mature...
Your passport:
Its expiry date is July eighty-six
But you hadn't needed visas for ages since—
See, impatiently, you couldn't wait to leave
So you boarded the gate in late eighty-three
Off to where there are no airfares,
Or cares...
Your passport:
Its number reads *74562*:
That's code for ***Forever, Dad, will I miss you***;
And since you didn't ever get to fly the route
You were meant to, I will claim the skies for you.

Homecoming.

Grief has a vast blast radius. Whenever there is a tragedy, it scatters everyone a huge distance from its immediate victims. When your father died, your mother told you that people were scared to go near her, now that she was a widow. Death's shame had tainted her.

Grief has thrown you a long way from a victim too. The first time you remember seeing your father, he was lying in a coffin and you were preparing for his funeral; the second time, you were awkwardly pushing the first handful of soil onto his grave; and this, thirty-five years later, is only the third memory you will have of being in his company.

You were only four that first time, so only parts of it are still vivid. The coffin was in the living room on the first floor of your house, the room was bustling with visitors; the floor tiles, tiny as pebbles, were a mosaic of sparkling white. To your left was the hall, its floor flamingo-pink, across which one afternoon a muscular cockroach scuttled faster than seemed fair or possible. Ahead of you was the balcony, upon whose windowsill you had tried to trap a lizard but had been left clutching only its tail, and along whose length you had chased what appeared to be a yellow peanut until it ran out of balcony and miraculously took flight.

Below was the garden, where a few days from now your own aunt would turn up with a lorry full of armed guards and rob her newly-buried brother's home at gunpoint, laughing as she went. You would run dov the adjacent staircase and slap her angrily on the side as she left anc would smile down at you out of the sun, the light framing her fac perhaps your first indication that halos are not reserved for angels. A few months later one of your security guards would be shot dead, but no one really who knows who did that, and a few years later, your aunt would turn up in London, having lost all the money she stole that day. She must have been spending that cash a long time.

Yet there was so much mischief within that radius too. There was the time your cousins tied the elastic of a tennis ball around the shed, so that whoever opened the door would see the elastic snap in front of their face, jumping back in shock. There was playing chase through fields of sugar canes that were three times your height, and occasionally stopping as you were being pursued so you could feast on your surroundings. There was the time you and your friends rode tricycles down their parents' driveway and terrifying speed, and they, suddenly seeing what was coming, leapt off their vehicles, and you, too late to change course, hit the kerb ahead of you and were catapulted headlong into a cactus. It would take their parents hours to remove every last one of the spikes.

In the years since, people would often ask you about Uganda, what it was like, and you would never really know what to say. If you had, you would have told them it was the place which taught you the extremes of joy and pain. And now, for better or worse, you are coming home.

***

Y[illegible]rive in Uganda just after one p.m. but you don't leave the airport till [illegible]lmost four. Wherever the country's government is spending its mone[illegible] is not here. The staff are utterly overwhelmed by the simultaneous arrival of three flights from Doha, Nairobi and Dubai, and the visa queues stretch back almost as far as the tarmac of the runway. There are four separate lines and the one for Ugandan citizens is by far the longest—there are more of them, yet at the same time their documents seem to be processed more slowly. You wait for your baggage in the hall, and it takes over two hours for all of your family's belongings to emerge. During that time you see hundreds of tightly-bound packages roll past you—they are wrapped in opaque tape, the names of their owners spelled out in dark blue marker. Luxury goods, says your mother. They go to Dubai and they cannot buy enough of them.

You stop by the exit of the airport, waiting for your mother to withdraw some of the local currency, and the cashpoint swallows her card. That is the third time that has happened today, says a nearby official. Why didn't you warn me not to use it, asks your mother, to which the official has no answer.

You step outside. The airport concourse is staffed by a handful of armed men trying to look important. Stand here, they say, ushering you a few yards from the main doors of the airport. Wait here for your taxi. You comply, and look up at the stone staircase which rises towards the departures section. It is cracked and yellowing, stained by tearful trails of brown rainwater. It has the standard of maintenance you would expect from an abandoned and deeply rural train station.

Your driver arrives, cheerful. It's the kind of attitude you need when facing Easter Friday traffic towards Kampala. As you get into the Land Rover and head out to the main road, you begin to drift into sleep, and your mother urges you to stay awake. You are missing Uganda, don't you want to see it, she asks, but fatigue has other ideas.

When you wake you are near the edge of town. A convoy of vehicles—a handful of motorcycles, two black cars with tinted windows—surges past you towards the airport. That must have been a government minister, says your mother, that is how they travel. If it was the President, there could have been twenty cars.

That night, before starting the long journey north, you dine at your uncle's house. Kampala reminds you of those summer afternoons as a child when you attached the garden hose to the tap, and then turned it up to full power; the city thrashes about, and sooner or later you are caught in the spray of one of its wild coils. Your uncle lives in one of the quieter loops, on a hill just above the middle of the city, the roads to his home a soothing carpet of clay. You last saw him almost exactly half a lifetime ago, when you were twenty, and grey is visiting your beard almost as regularly as his.

You're now at an age where your uncle speaks freely with you, and you only wish this moment had come sooner. This is the first visit where you truly understand your family's elder members, why they always seemed so distracted by their past in a country you had spent decades fleeing from. Maybe that's the irony of many a second-generation immigrant; it's your parents who ran, but it's you who continues running long after they have come to rest.

For the longest time, you couldn't work out why your uncle was so obsessed with Uganda, why he couldn't just let it go for the prosperity he had found in the West. You know now that it was responsibility—because your uncle knew that for every person like him there were thousands who had not made it out, whom the army had given just three days to leave their homes with whatever they could carry and if they had refused to do so were shot on sight. Your uncle knew that there were hundreds of thousands more, almost two million more at their peak, who were marched at gunpoint into the countryside, far from any source of food, water or sanitation, and, circled by rifles, were left to die. For twenty-five years, just a few hundred kilometres to the south, your uncle has slowly and patiently worked with dozens of survivors, a cluster of others who made it out, to bring an end to this slow-motion genocide and make the best of its aftermath.

This is what your uncle has long been worried about: that the mass murder of your people would quickly be followed by an attempt to deny that they were ever there. That is why he has forever been occupied with a land dispute, crawling its way through the courts. It is one of the defining acts of his life and you have barely discussed it with him till now, but now that you are of age there is no need to. It instantly makes sense, because you understand that your whole life you have been fighting your own small version of his struggle too.

Your visit to your uncle's place is the first true stage of your homecoming, a dinner of maize meal, spinach, peanut butter and chicken. Afterwards, you begin the journey north, at the start of which it takes you two hours just to leave a frantic Kampala. Each last seat of the matatus, those Seventies-style camper vans that double as local taxis, is crammed with passengers.

Your drive north is as calming as watching a baby sleep while tied to its mother's back. Your drive back south will be far less comfortable, given that you will share most of it in the back seat with a frightened chicken who your driver has bought for his mother, and who at various points seems determined to jump from its basket and attack anyone in sight in its bid for freedom. What if you fall asleep and you wake up only to find it is clawing out your eyes? This is why you will not fall asleep on your journey home.

You move north, the busy city becoming a two-lane highway little more than eight metres wide. Every half hour or so you are overtaken by a coach coloured as brightly as a fairground ride; that's the express bus, soaring through the night at near-impossible velocity. You'd not dare set foot on that thing. Its windows are apparently tinted, as if to shield its passengers from the danger of their journey, their vessel passing only inches from disaster along the narrow road. To travel at those speeds, the drivers must have traded their own souls.

That's not nearly the most risky form of travel, though. One lorry ahead of you carries bales of hay, which are strapped to the back of its open-top trailer, which is really nothing more than two sets of steel railings. On top of those bales are three people; one of whom is clinging to those railings, while the other two are sprawled across the hay, blissfully asleep. The slightest collision with any onrushing vehicle, and at least those latter two are dead.

As your vehicle rattles upwards through the country, you see a series of one-storey settlements pass on either side of you, bungalows clustered like horses rushing to drink from a stream. Beyond them, stretching away far past the moonlight, is the bottomless forest. It's funny: when you're in the West, you're a city-dweller, but when you're in the North of Uganda, you feel a greater affinity for the rural. The moment you left Kampala's orbit, you felt relieved. Your driver lets you know that you are approaching Karuma, the bridge that passes over the River Nile, and you draw down your window just in time so you can smell it, the salty sharpness roaming your nostrils. You look down at the river, a silver ribbon weaving its way down through the dark, and conclude that the Nile must look best by night.

You arrive in your mother's hometown just after midnight. You are sleeping when you get there, and are woken by a gentle tapping on the window. You step out of the vehicle and find everyone else standing in a small clearing, next to a proud parade of trees. A woman steps forward, her handshake light as a rose. Welcome home, she says. It has been such a long time. You later learn that she is in her mid-fifties, which you would have thought impossible if you had not met her adult children.

When people greet you here, no one squeezes your hand hard like they do in Berlin, and it takes a couple of days for you to adjust. You don't know why you expected the Ugandan handshake to be more aggressive— maybe because, life has been more brutal up here than most places. But you will soon be reminded that people in the North are tough, not macho.

Your mother is staying here, on the edge of town, in the same simple living quarters she has been visiting for the last few years. Her accommodation here is a small brick building, not much larger than her bedroom back in England, and whose corrugated tin roof was blown off by a storm just last week. She lives here alongside the woman and her family, one of dozens whose education and living costs she has been supporting for the last two decades. You know now why your mother and her siblings always seemed so distracted, so exhausted—because they never really left Uganda, were always drained by thoughts of those they had left behind.

You are staying in the middle of town, in a hotel that is one of the better ones in the city, your mother clearly trying to ease you back into life back here. Your hotel backs onto an evangelical church which, though it is now about two a.m., is hosting a service in full swing, the pastor refusing to let God's enemies rest. Your bed must be no more than twenty metres from his pulpit, and so you can hear him and his euphoric audience through the wall, thundering and successive waves of praise and amens. Despite this clamour, though, within five minutes you are asleep.

***

The next day you rest, then run a few small errands in town. That night you arrive back at the hotel, the rain clattering down, and you are grateful for the cool evening. Due to the day's heavy heat, you have been sweating slowly almost since you woke that morning. You slide quickly into bed, and into sleep.

A few hours later you wake. You can't see anything, since there are no streetlights overlooking your narrow courtyard, but you can hear something: the high, excited buzzing of two mosquitoes. You can't tell how close they are. You quietly grow anxious. There is a mosquito net over your bed, hanging low like the roof of a festival tent, but you're not sure it can repel the invaders. This is because, just before you lay down that evening, you noticed a hole in the net—not large, but big enough for an enterprising and blood-hungry creature of the night to pass through.

The buzzing continues, and the next few minutes are spent in a form of Ugandan roulette. Do you stay in bed, as still as you can, and hope that the mosquitoes do not find the hole? Or do you go on the attack, tearing aside the net and with it your fear, lighting your righteous path with your smartphone, gathering up a towel and swatting these winged fiends down? You make the calculation. If you throw off your shield and hunt them, then you expose your entire body to them at once, giving them a vast surface area on which to feast. All they have to do is make one puncture, and the day is lost. If you take a defensive approach, then you must wait in hours of quiet terror till the morning, knowing that at any moment these beasts may discover that passage to the treasures of your flesh.

You stay still for many minutes. The buzzing comes. At last you can bear it no longer. You must be bold. You roll under the net to the cold floor—for a few moments you are flying sightless, a spaceman in the vacuum without a helmet—and then your phone is in your hand, your way is lit, the chase is afoot.

Such is the fury of your emergence that for some time you do not notice that the buzzing has ceased. Perhaps the mosquitoes are in hiding. Yet as the silence eases onwards, you conclude that they have sunk back into the chaotic folds of the night whence they came. This is your victory—it is surely you who has forced them to retreat. Exhausted from his heroic exertions, the lion returns to the lair beneath his net, and there he sleeps.

***

Your great-uncle, who once escaped a firing-squad the night before he was due to be shot, tells you a story. Whenever he talks, you frown, and he then pauses, possibly concerned that he is irritating you. He is wrong: instead, you are concentrating so that you can absorb whatever he says with every available part of your body.

The story took place fifteen years ago. Your uncle, his nephew, was travelling back to Uganda to see some members of his family. At the airport, your uncle ran into an old schoolfriend, who had by then achieved some status in the military. Where are you heading, the soldier asked. Up North, said my uncle, who as always was genial but quietly wary. Me too, said the soldier, let's go in my helicopter. So they flew up there, to one of the country's glorious national parks. As they flew, they passed over thousands of huts fashioned from straw and mud by desperate and starving human beings. Look down there, said the soldier to my uncle, pointing with pride at the concentration camps below. These people do not know how to take care of the land, they are wasting it. So we are waiting until we have wiped them out and then we will take all of it. My uncle listened, and then they landed and went their separate ways.

A few days later, my uncle called the soldier. That place you flew over in the helicopter, he said, that's the land that belonged to my people, and those people you said you wanted to wipe out, those were my people.

That was only a joke, said the soldier, I was only joking.

It was a very serious joke, said my uncle. Anyway, not to worry. Let's get a drink soon. Yes, when are you leaving, asked the soldier. In three days, said my uncle, knowing full well that he was flying out that same night, and who then hung up the phone and promptly left the country.

That's why you listen whenever your great-uncle speaks; because, after ten minutes or so, he always starts telling stories like this.

***

You hadn't seen your great-uncle in over a decade, and so he has been very eager to see you; that's why he has invited you round the day after your arrival. Back in the Seventies, before conflict came to Uganda, he was a famous radio producer. During the war, he escaped to Sweden; and now that many of his opponents are gone, having died wealthy, free and remorseless, he has returned.

For the last four months, he has been staying here, in a residence comprised of two bungalows; one with a living room and bathroom, the other with a dining room, bathroom and bedroom. Between the two bungalows is a large garden, where you find him sitting in the shade of mango trees. Two dogs and a convoy of chickens wander through a gap in the fence and onto my great-uncle's property; you are surprised to see dogs and chickens getting on so well, and you theorise that maybe they have formed an alliance against their common enemy the fox, who is nowhere in sight.

Your great-uncle, by now in his mid-eighties, has been busy. He is currently working on what he calls "public relations"—settling back into life in the North, and generally just being a listening ear in the community. Yet he always commands an audience; whenever he sits down at a public event, a circle of chairs forms around him. That afternoon, he tells you a selection of stories from the war years, each of them new to you, and then—as a tropical storm rolls down out of nowhere—you stop for an early dinner. After your meal, you walk through the garden to settle your stomach, and—just behind your great-uncle's home, no more than twenty metres from where he rests his head each night—you find the grave of his most beloved sister, next to that of her youngest daughter and her grand-daughter. My God, you think, how much he still misses them, how much you miss them; and then you reflect that, here up North, there is quite literally a piece of your past around every corner.

***

Money. So many people here ask you for it, and maybe that shouldn't be a surprise. They know the cost of that smartphone in your hand, they see you pay for a whole tank of fuel as if it were nothing to you. Everything is money, it seems. How can it not be? For them, you are in a position to address so many specific needs. A laptop for work, some backing to start a business. The requests are frequent and varied. Some arrive as casual requests at the start of a short conversation, some come tucked within envelopes following a church service, and some come at the end of compelling stories, a dream with a price tag attached. In each case you tell them the same thing. You would love to help, you say, but you must be very careful in what you give, because you do not have very much money by the standards of where you live and so you need to be focused, otherwise you may run out of cash.

You have only been here two days but you already feel strange things happening to your sense of reality. In Berlin you were recently so broke that you were afraid to check your bank balance, yet here you are affluent enough to change someone's entire month for the better. You are constantly asked what investments you will make in the community, what projects you will launch and develop. This person says you are their brother now, this person calls you their father, both of them want you to take care of them financially. I am not your brother, you tell one of them, I already have one of those, and I am not your father, you tell another one of them, you are older than me. Don't run away from me, don't leave me, they tell you.

You again regret not having made millions of pounds when you had the chance. If you had pursued a career in financial services you could have been truly wealthy by now—you could have come back here and made a genuine difference, instead of feeling a little like the fraud you do now. Or maybe you are kidding yourself—maybe you never had the discipline to sit at a computer for twenty years in a mile-high office block, to bite your tongue in a boardroom. You were always too loud, too chaotic for that. Look at the things you do for a living—poetry, journalism, music. It is almost laughable how allergic you are to making money. No, there is no alternate reality where you are some corporate titan. This is always who you were going to be.

***

Religion is everything here. You think back to those times in white Western Europe when you have heard people making fun of evangelical church services, mocking the hollering pastors, and how you laughed along with them. But of course the praise of the Lord must be more vigorous, of course God is louder here. The stakes are so much higher. Of course church is calmer in white Western Europe. In West Germany there is a God of universal healthcare, in Switzerland there is a God of casual affluence. In those churches, God long ago came good, but here in Northern Uganda he has long ago needed all the help he can get. Unlike those places of worship you have seen elsewhere, where preachers speak from dreary and carefully-prepared scripts, these pastors work like battle rappers, freestyling their sermons over a soaring chorus from their congregation—we arrest every strategy of the Devil, Lord Jesus, we brandish the banner of your faith, Lord Jesus, no usurper can stand against you, Lord Jesus—the momentum of their words unstoppable, carrying them through war after war. In white Western Europe, you have the luxury of seeing Christianity as just another religion, as just one more route to enlightenment, but here it is the very fuel of survival.

***

The following morning you all set off early for your father's village, getting out of bed at five a.m. and hitting the road north by six. The drive is just over a hundred kilometres but it will take you two hours, your three-strong convoy of Land Rovers hammering its way over countless speed bumps. You knew it before you arrived, you saw it last time you were here, but still: the poverty. On your way you see thousands of people who look just like you standing outside buildings which have received no investment in decades. Rusty signs announce that primary schools are still under construction. The last stretch of road to that village is little more than a dirt track, a blanket of thick red dust reshaped by each passing tyre.

There were six hundred NGOs here, you say to your brother. What did they do while they were here? Where is the infrastructure? You calm down, then. Maybe those NGOs are the reason many of these people on the streets are still alive. You redirect your anger, then. You remind yourself that this is exactly what dysfunctional governments do—they do nothing for so long that you not only no longer expect nothing from them, you forget they were ever there. You are standing here getting angry at charities, while there are hundreds of millionaire ministers who haven't given a thought to this region in years.

When you get to your father's village, your driver is at first unsure where you are going—though he is from this region, this is very far north even for him—and so he stops to ask a passer-by for directions. Well, laughs the passer-by, if you carry on for another twenty minutes you'll end up in another country. You laugh too, then. They used to joke that your father was born so close to the border he was effectively Sudanese, and, here is your evidence.

The driver turns round and you come to the main square, which has a marquee and a long stage along two sides, faced by a large and expectant crowd, perhaps seven hundred people. First the local bishop will conduct a two-hour mass, then there will be another hour of speeches, including one from you, about what your homecoming means for the village. You sit beside your mother, great-uncle and brother in the marquee, in the first of eight or so rows; as if seeing you as easy prey in your black jacket and grey trousers, the sun quickly turns its focus towards you.

You have never spoken your native tongue that well, and so you only catch about ten per cent of what is said, your eyes having to translate the rest. There is gratitude for your mother's large donation to the local church, the master of ceremonies plucking the cash from the envelope and holding it aloft. There is an offer of communion and the grant of many blessings, the warmth of traditional hymns. There is a nod towards you from the leader of your clan as he rises to speak, the gist of his address being, good on you for coming back here, many people would have avoided it. It is now your turn to address the audience, and taking the wireless microphone, you move to the middle of the square, a translator standing nearby. This is what you tell them.

So here we are at last: my brother and I, representing our family, to see you, and to see our father. I am a writer, and so it is my job to find the right words. But, right now, I can't think of a job more difficult.

The last time I saw my father I buried him. That is my first memory of him, and so for a very long time I was afraid of this day. Now, though, I am almost excited.

When I buried him, I was too young to say goodbye, but now the only word I want to say is Hello.

So, hello father. It has been thirty-six years. I am nearly forty, which is the age you were when you died. I am here with my brother, representing our siblings, and we hope that we have made you proud. Life has not always been easy, but we keep pushing forwards, we keep trying to be good people.

Some people will ask why I have not been here earlier. The truth is that I was scared. You did so much before you died, and then you died too young. And so, for most of my life, I have been scared of one thing: that I would not achieve enough in the time that was given to me.

But now I realise that was the wrong way to think. Life isn't about climbing as high as you can—life is about circles. It's about coming back to the places where parts of you belong, and part of me will always belong here. To be here today, I have travelled a circle the size of the world. I have travelled through love, through cities, through countries. And through it all, I have carried your name, as close to me as my passport. I have taken your name into every lecture hall, into every news interview, onto every stage, so that whoever sees it can know—look, there goes Northern Uganda.

And now we have come full circle. My brother and I have carried your name back to your village. At first I worried that we had not done enough work to be worthy of you. But then I realised: that is the good thing about work, maybe the best thing: that the work is never finished. Your work was not finished, and neither will be ours. But we promise you Father that we are doing it, and that we always will.

There is polite applause and you return to your seat. A lorry pulls up and a group of catering staff unload several tables, on which they place the trays of that afternoon's meal. The children, silent throughout despite hours of listening, shift in excitement. This is, after all, the day's culmination, the true moment of village unity: the joy when food is served.

After eating, you begin the short walk from the centre of the village, towards the burial place. Dozens of locals are already standing there, surrounding it, awaiting your arrival. As you approach, the crowd parts and there it is, ten metres away: your father's grave. At once, you stop walking. Your hands rush to the bridge of your nose, but your tears get there first. A hand arrives on your shoulder and you stand there weeping. As you open your eyes, the singing begins. You don't know who started it, but within seconds everyone seems to have joined in; it is a low, mournful yet rousing sound, somewhere between a lament and a lullaby.

They maintain that same volume as you approach the grave, as if knowing your grief is already so public that further loudness would cruelly intrude. The grave is a long and broad rectangular slab of white stone, just under longer and wider than the coffin you remember in your living room thirty-five years ago. On top of the grave is a headstone about a metre long, raised at a forty-five degree incline. It bears your father's name and date of death, just eighteen days before his forty-first birthday; it lists his full professional qualifications and army rank, lieutenant colonel chief medical superintendent head of military hospital mr doctor frcs ed consultant surgeon, and then the sentence that makes you proudest of all and by far, if not his motto then the code by which he lived, loved and died:

IF WE DO NOT START TO LIBERATE UGANDA THEN WHO WILL

There is no question mark, and somehow this feels all the more forceful for it. There is no shame in a failed revolution. The margins for error are so small, the rewards for success so enduring, that the bravery lies in making the attempt.

You walk around his grave, first kneeling and placing the palm of one hand on the graves of the family members buried next to him—his mother, his grandmother, his sister. Finally, as the crowd quietens down and thins out, knowing you must do this last part alone, you have come home.

Maybe, to you, home will always be a moment. For some, home is a building, an actual place, but for you it is a feeling, the handshake of an old friend or the embrace of a new one, the first mouthful of a meal cooked with love. For now, home is here, and never more so; home is this moment when you kneel to clutch the headstone of your father's grave, and shudder as you sob, your jacket buckling under the weight of the rain. You press your shoulder against his, not caring who sees you so raw; you don't know how long you rest there, perhaps only a few seconds, but you don't want to leave him. But of course you can't leave him—that's impossible. Not with all of him that is already in you.

You climb into the front passenger seat of your Land Rover and look back at your father. He doesn't look lonely there, you think. Look at him. He is surrounded by four generations of his family, and buried beneath the largest tree in the clearing. He has come to a majestic rest.

You take two photographs, because you will need to keep this moment. The photo does that beautiful thing where, each time you hold your thumb to your smartphone, it leaps into life for a couple of seconds—and so, for those instants, you are truly back in that time when you captured the shot. In that sense, you will never have to drive away from him again.

As the engine starts, you are surprised at how quickly the sadness passes. There is no melancholy, only a lightness. Journey's end, you think, this is the journey's end. You are not running anymore.

A couple of days later, you prepare to leave the north of Uganda. After an evening meal you say goodbye to your brother, who is staying at a hotel in town, and then you embrace first the local family who have been so supportive in your time there and finally your mother. I love you, she says, and for the first time in your life you remember telling her out loud, not via a Christmas card or book inscription or text message, that you love her too.

And finally you are free; in the end, it was all about love. You are not running anymore; imagine what you can do with all that energy you once spent escaping. You are suddenly aware of a strange and new sense of contentment, as if your spirit has taken the last few days digesting an immense meal, and now your soul is full. Your soul is full. Your vehicle circles round the yard, draws out of the field and indicates to its right, and then begins the slow descent towards Kampala.

Rough Trade Books is a publishing venture in the mould of the pioneering independent record label—aiming to bring the same radical spirit to the world of books.

Rough Trade Small Books are, on one level, exactly as they sound—neat, pocket-sized books. Small but perfectly formed. That kind of thing.

On the other hand, they are big ideas, bold thinking, works of boundless imagination, and infinite scope.

We hope that they are as accessible as our Rough Trade Editions, and as wide-ranging, but with a few more pages of all that good stuff we try to provide.

roughtradebooks.com

A SHORT HISTORY
ROOF DOG
OF THE WIND MILL
WILL HODGKINSON

Roof Dog: A Short History of The Windmill

Will Hodgkinson

The Windmill is a flat-roofed pub in Brixton that for the past two decades has been at the epicentre of the capital's underground music scene. Everyone from Mica Levi to Fat White Family to Black Midi has passed through its doors, which are presided over by a series of roof dogs including the legendary Ben the Rottweiler. With the help of impressionistic sketches by his son Otto, Will Hodgkinson goes on a spiritual journey to the heart of the Windmill, seeking to understand why this former Irish boozer has become such a magical space of freedom and discovery.

ENYA

A TREATISE
ON UNGUILTY
PLEASURES

CHILLY GONZALES

Enya: A Treatise on Unguilty Pleasures
Chilly Gonzales

Chilly Gonzales is one of the most exciting, original, hard-to-pin-down musicians of our time. Filling halls worldwide at the piano in his slippers and a bathrobe—in any one night he can be dissecting the musicology of an Oasis hit, giving a sublime solo recital, and displaying his lyrical dexterity as a rapper. In his book about ENYA, he asks: Does music have to be smart or does it just have to go to the heart? In dazzling, erudite prose Gonzales delves beyond her innumerable gold discs and millions of fans to excavate his own enthusiasm for ENYA's singular music as well as the mysterious musician herself, and along the way uncovers new truths about the nature of music, fame, success and the artistic endeavour.

ACKNOWLEDGEMENTS

For my father, and for my mother, who urged me to go and see him;

For Jennifer Neal, an extraordinary writer and an even better human being;

For the late, great and beloved Mac Folkes, who was as Berlin as they come.

I would also like to thank:
My agent Abi Fellows at the Good Literary Agency, Nina Hervé and Will Burns at Rough Trade Books, Craig Oldham, Miriam, Sarah Maslin Nir, Rhea Schmitt, Julia Kingsford, Ryan Hunn, Joshua Aaron, Lee Davis, Elena Barschazki, Steffi Hirsbrunner, Jessica Lauren Elizabeth Taylor, Magdalena Dehmel, Brandi Geurkink, Hannah Grünewald, Clara Gutteridge, Ruby Russell, Maja Sinn, Jessica Horn, Bror Sander Berg Størseth, Isaiah Lopaz, Fernanda Cury Cabral, Kat Anderson, Taiye Selasi, Samir Ibrahim, Krisz Kreuzer, Tahir Della, Michael Ohst, Yasmina Banaszczuk, Kirsty Simmonds, Reba Mangope, Oliver Schmitt, Mayowa Lynette, Leila Essa, Dave Gordon, Orla Baumgarten, Zoe Cooper, Louise Aldridge, Friederike Busch, Sharon Dodua Otoo, Charlott Schönwetter, Ben Rollman, Clarissa von Bormann, Thao Nguyen, Eun-Hae Seetang, Luciana Sodré Murdoch Fernandes, Carlos Murdoch, Thomaz Ambrosio, Matheus Sodré, Maissa Lihedheb, Vinay Patel, Anna Jäger, Mark Ivan Mukiibi Serunjogi, Tara Hawk, Nishant Kumar, Nikesh Shukla, Inua Ellams, Soja Subhagar, Amelia Ideh, Jamie McKelvie, Gerdi Bauer, Alex Todorovic, Marijana Todorovic, Burcu Güvenç, Jonathan Harding, Jumoké Fashola, Elizabeth Schumacher, Andrew Weber, David Felipe, Paul French, Alex Wright, Adam Shingleton, The Unicorns, and The Council of Good Friends.

MUSA OKWONGA

Musa Okwonga is a writer, broadcaster and musician. The co-host of the Stadio football podcast, he has published one collection of poetry and three books about football, the first of which, *A Cultured Left Foot*, was nominated for the 2008 William Hill Sports Book of the Year Award. His work has appeared in various outlets, including Africa Is A Country, Byline Times, Foreign Policy, The Guardian, The New York Times, The Economist and The Ringer. He lives in Berlin.

roughtradebooks.com